RATIONING AND RATIONALITY
IN THE NATIONAL HEALTH SERVICE

ECONOMIC ISSUES IN HEALTH CARE

General editors

Professor Gavin Mooney
Health Economics Research Unit
Dept of Public Health
Medical School
Aberdeen AN9 2ZD

Dr Alistair McGuire
Dept of Sociological Studies
Wolfson College
University of Oxford
Oxford OX2 6UD

The Challenges of Medical Practice Variations
Edited by Tavs Folmer Andersen and Gavin Mooney (1990)

Private Exchange and Public Interest
By John Forbes (1990)

Rationing and Rationality in the National Health Service
Edited by Stephen J. Frankel and R. R. West (1993)

Just Managing – Power and Culture in the NHS
By Stephen Harrison, David J. Hunter, Gordon Marnoch
and Christopher Pollitt (1993)

Dental Care: An Economic View
By David Parkin and Brian Yule (1990)

RATIONING
AND
RATIONALITY
IN THE NATIONAL
HEALTH SERVICE

The Persistence of Waiting Lists

Edited by

Stephen Frankel

and

Robert West

MACMILLAN

First published 1993 by
THE MACMILLAN PRESS LTD
Houndmills, Basingstoke, Hampshire RG21 2XS
and London
Companies and representatives
throughout the world

ISBN 0–333–49006–1 hardcover
ISBN 0–333–49007–X paperback

A catalogue record for this book is available
from the British Library

Copy-edited and typeset by Cairns Craig Editorial, Edinburgh

Printed in Hong Kong

Contents

List of Tables and Figures

TABLES

FIGURES

List of Contributors

John Cullis
School of Social Sciences
University of Bath
Claverton Down
Bath BA2 7AY.

Stephen Farrow
Barnet Health Authority
Colindale Hospital
Colindale Avenue
London NW9 5HG.

Stephen Frankel
Health Care Evaluation Unit
Department of Epidemiology and Public Health Medicine
Canynge Hall
Whiteladies Road
Bristol BS8 2PR.

Ian Harvey
Health Care Evaluation Unit,
Department of Epidemiology and Public Health Medicine,
Canynge Hall
Whiteladies Road
Bristol BS8 2PR.

David Jewell
General Practice Unit
Department of Epidemiology and Public Health Medicine
Canynge Hall
Whiteladies Road
Bristol BS8 2PR.

Margaret Robbins
Health Care Evaluation Unit
Department of Epidemiology and Public Health Medicine
Canynge Hall
Whiteladies Road
Bristol BS8 2PR.

Robert West
Department of Epidemiology and Community Medicine
University of Wales College of Medicine
Heath Park
Cardiff CF4 4XN.

CHAPTER 1

The Origins of Waiting Lists

Stephen Frankel

The central observation underlying this book is that the National Health Service (NHS) appears to have selected for relative neglect those few conditions where treatments are unequivocally effective, can be delivered at comparatively low cost, and are desired by the population. This outcome for over forty years' investment in health care would appear to fail any simple criteria of rationality.

All health systems are now compelled to address the question of what are the true priorities amongst the range and volume of services which might ideally be provided. The broad thrust of the health economist's argument – that rational grounds must be sought for allocating finite resources in the face of overwhelming demands – is now broadly accepted. The current debate is concerned almost exclusively with how to make choices in resource allocation, rather than whether choices should be made. This intellectual consensus is now broken only by those philosophers who point to the conflict between utilitarianism and the rights of individuals (Harris, 1988). The implication of the health economist's argument – that explicit rationing is preferable to the implicit rationing which characterises all health systems – is politically more contentious, but this too has been expressed in policy initiatives, both in the United States (Oregon Health Services Commission, 1991) and in Britain (Dean, 1991).

The National Health Service was established as a 'comprehensive health service designed to secure improvement in the physical and mental health of the people . . . and the prevention, diagnosis and treatment of illness', and to do so 'free of charge' (NHS Act, 1946). Prior to the establishment of the NHS, health care rationing was determined by income, employment status and sex. Subsequent to its establishment, rationing for certain treatments has been ordered by willingness to wait. Waiting lists offer a device for blurring the boundaries of available provision by offering treatments where there may be no prospect that these treatments will be delivered. The recent reorganisation of the NHS (National Health Service and Community Care Act, 1990) was intended to redirect activity

1

towards those areas which may better reflect health needs, as these are perceived by the population, and so make explicit the limits to the care which may be offered. This process cannot succeed unless the wider influences upon the balance of care are acknowledged.

AIMS OF THIS ANALYSIS

The issue of waiting for treatment in the National Health Service has spawned a voluminous literature. The question must therefore be posed: why another analysis? While the text of this volume must provide its own justification, the nature of its intended contribution can be made explicit at the outset. The existing literature on waiting lists spans economic analyses, epidemiological studies of waiting patients, comments on the limitations of waiting list statistics, management proposals for waiting list reduction, political polemics and consumer guides. However the degree of engagement between these various viewpoints can be limited, so that many previous analyses have tended to approach the problem in a piecemeal fashion.

The contention underlying this book is that this enduring phenomenon offers the most graphic evidence that resources for clinical intervention are not directed in the most rational manner. Waiting lists should therefore be considered as one expression of the implicit priorities of the health service. An understanding of waiting lists, and the design of measures which may succeed in their alleviation, must therefore draw on the widest context of public health, which must accommodate health economics and that branch of epidemiology concerned with health care evaluation, as well as historical perspectives on the development of the health service.

Following the broad interpretation of waiting lists in this chapter, and the view of the health economist in the second, the bulk of the book mirrors the sequence followed by patients when gaining access to specialist care. The waiting list issue is thus analysed in sequence in terms of the broad need for health care, in relation to the organisation of primary care, in the context of access to outpatient assessment and in terms of access to inpatient hospital services.

THE PERSISTENCE OF WAITING LISTS

The nature and content of waiting for treatment in the National Health Service has remained remarkably stable since the inception of the service, and yet much writing about waiting lists implies that the phenomenon is an aberration which demands ready solutions. Waiting lists are intermittently regarded as constituting some sort of crisis, usually a political crisis. The response to these crises is some sort of 'initiative' (for example, Ministry of Health, 1962; Ministry of Health, 1963; Department of Health and Social Security, 1975; Health Services Board, 1977). Perhaps the most generous initiative to date is the £50 000 000 waiting-list fund announced in November 1986 (Anonymous, 1987b).

Newspaper reports change little from decade to decade, recycled rather like the 'dog bites baby' story of the popular press. This is not just a British phenomenon. With characteristic Australian gusto, Best (1987) bemoans 'the tragic fact of modern-day health care that the only measure that the average politician – especially when in opposition – has of health care is the waiting-list. The response resembles the Moro reflex: every time that politicians hear a complaint about the length of waiting-lists for surgery, they fling their arms about wide in horror and dart for the nearest pen to write a media release.'

It is interesting to note that the current reorganisation of the NHS has its origin in such a perceived crisis. It therefore appears that the most radical restructuring of the NHS to date has been led by perceived failings in the small part of the service which deals with elective surgery. After forty years the waiting list tail has finally succeeded in wagging the entire NHS dog. While this initiative may succeed in alleviating the waiting list, or at least in concealing it, to date the various initiatives have produced little measurable change.

The examination of waiting lists over time affirms the need for humility before suggesting that a particular initiative will lead to significant improvements in patient access. Waiting lists have remained remarkably constant throughout the history of the NHS. The numbers may have risen, but as a percentage of total throughput there has been little change (Figure 1.1).

With this degree of stability, it may appear more reasonable to consider waiting lists as an attribute rather than as an anomaly of the National Health Service. In many other fields of social life public perceptions may shift where the phenomenon in question remains constant. Policy can be formulated in response to perceived changes where no objective change may have occurred. Current views of mob violence would appear to be of this sort, for example. Levels of violence would appear to be relatively constant, while public perceptions of a breakdown of the social order intermittently produce political responses (Pearson, 1983). Another example comes from the popular perception of major changes in the dominant family form. This perception of change has to be set against the evidence from historical sociology that a pattern of persistence rather than change emerges from empirical studies. Peter Laslett (1977) uses the word perdurance to underline this persistence. Waiting lists have

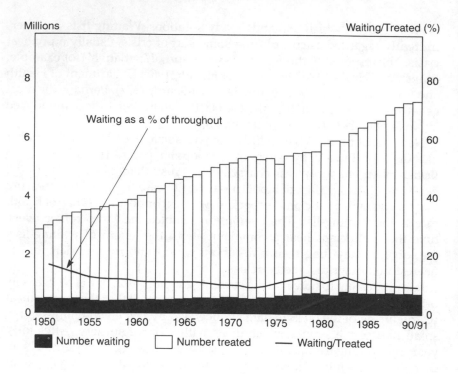

Millions   Waiting/Treated (%)

Figure 1.1 Inpatient waiting lists and hospital throughput, England

only existed in their current form for decades rather than centuries. Nevertheless it is reasonable to talk of the perdurance of waiting lists, particularly as many features of the modern service have been set by the nature of previous provision.

THE NATURE OF WAITING AS DISTINCT FROM THE FACT OF WAITING

Some commentators have been led by this perdurance of waiting lists to conclude that there is very little that can be done. Enoch Powell (1966: 40) reflected sardonically in his memoirs on the ‧effort he expended, as Minister of Health, in 'trying to get the waiting lists down. It is an activity about as hopeful as filling a sieve . . . In a medical service free at the point of consumption the waiting lists, like the poor in the Gospel, are always with us . . . *Naturam expellas furca, tamen usque recurret*: though you drive Nature out with a pitchfork, she will still find her way back'.

The number of 'waiting list initiatives' and their relative failure might suggest that there is little that can be done. This view is also the

Table 1.1 Patients on selected in-patient waiting lists
at 31 March 1991 (as percentages of total and specialty throughput)

	Number on waiting list	Cumulative percentage of total waiting list	Waiting list as a percentage of specialty throughput
General surgery	140 300	20	14
Trauma/orthopaedic	130 000	39	23
Ear, nose, and throat	102 000	54	36
Gynaecology	83 800	66	14
Ophthalmology	82 200	78	47

Source Government Statistical Service, 1991b

conclusion of much economic analysis, for example by Frost (1980). It is inevitable that the lack of a price barrier in the NHS must lead to some implicit or explicit problem of proximate access to treatment for some conditions. However, it is a central tenet of this volume that the fact of waiting must be distinguished from the nature of waiting. The necessary fact that all people may not have ready access to all treatments does not imply that particular people from particular neighbourhoods with particular conditions must wait many years for a particular operation. It is in these details that key clues to the nature of the waiting list problem lie.

The first observation, which calls into question the treatment of inpatient waiting lists as an expression of global deficiencies within the NHS, is the fact that waiting lists are largely accounted for by a few specialties only. The figures shown in Table 1.1 indicate that just under one half of waiting occurs in the two specialties of general surgery and trauma and orthopaedic surgery. A further quarter occurs in the three specialties of ear, nose and throat surgery, gynaecology and ophthalmology.

Nevertheless, even in those specialties where there are large lists, as a percentage of total throughput we are looking at the equivalent of only a few weeks' to a few months' admissions. The percentages shown in Table 1 include all those on waiting lists. The pejorative tone of the term waiting list is inappropriate for many of these cases, as it is quite proper for work to be scheduled in advance to allow the efficient use of specialist facilities as well as to allow people to make their own domestic and professional preparations. It is therefore worth dwelling on those categories of waiting which are clearly unacceptable.

Without question it is unacceptable for patients to wait over one year for treatments they have been promised. Many people appear to be in this unacceptable predicament. According to Department of Health figures, on 31 March 1991 a total of 169 800 people had waited over one year for treatment (Government Statistical Service, 1991b). In considering these cases it is important to remember that many of those classified as waiting

Table 1.2   Critical categories of patients on selected in-patient waiting lists at 31 March 1991 (as percentages of 1989/90 throughput)

	Non-urgent >1 year %
General surgery	3
Trauma and orthopaedic	5
Ear, nose and throat	6
Gynaecology	2
Ophthalmology	7

Source   Government Statistical Service, 1991b and 1990.

'over one year' have waited for several years and that an unknown but significant proportion of these patients are never to be treated at all.

Again these cases may appear to represent a major indictment of the NHS as a whole until we consider them in relation to the throughput in the relevant specialties (Table 1.2). Statistics for 'urgent cases waiting over one month' are no longer published, but in the last year for which these figures are available – 1987 – such urgent cases represented between 0.3 to 2% of annual throughput for these same specialties (DHSS 1987). It is clear that these critical categories of waiters represent only a few days' to a few weeks' work, depending on the specialty.

If these groups of untreated patients were symptomatic of any general mismatch between resources and demand, one might expect some correlation between waiting times and a range of available district level measures of provision, resource and socio-economic variables. Such correlations have been examined by Harley (1988) in relation to trauma and orthopaedic surgery. The lack of any such correlations is striking.

The use of waiting list statistics to expose global deficiencies in the NHS becomes yet less convincing when we consider the clinical composition of these lists. The importance of an intimate examination of waiting lists in seeking to explain them has been established largely through the work of John Yates and his co-workers at the Inter-Authority Comparisons and Consultancy Unit of the Health Services Management Centre, University of Birmingham (for example, Yates, 1987). Long waits occur mainly in relation to a few conditions. Not only are waiting lists largely accounted for by a few specialties, but within those specialties almost half of those waiting require one of a very few operations (Davidge *et al.*, 1987). In the main these people want surgery for their varicose veins, hernias, painful or immobile joints, cataracts and enlarged tonsils, or they are women awaiting sterilisation.

The question about waiting lists is then not simply 'Why are they waiting?' It is, 'Why are these people with these particular conditions waiting so long to be treated within these specialties?'. This brief outline of waiting list statistics therefore indicates that what we actually have is not a general delay in treating all people, but instead a process of selecting from the mainstream of patients a separate and relatively small population of waiters.

The metaphor of the mainstream can usefully be pursued. We are not dealing with a simple queue where the flow of demand is dammed back by banks that are too narrow. The formation of waiting lists corresponds more with the development of an ox-bow lake. The meandering flow succeeds in taking a short cut, and so leaves an isolated lake. Similarly, the flow of acute care finds a way of isolating a selected portion of the demand upon it. The alternative term for an ox-bow lake, mortlake, offers a more graphic metaphor for the pool of demand that is set to one side in this way. In the mortlake of the waiting list we isolate a proportion of the cases of piles, hernias, varicose veins, cataracts and bad hips to flounder as well as they can, unless they choose, or can afford, to buy their way out.

We have seen that, in relation to the whole range of activities within the NHS, those who wait exceptionally long periods for these procedures represent a relatively trivial burden. Before we can make sense of solutions to this problem, solutions which may or may not require additional resources, it is important to pause and consider how this seemingly unnecessary predicament came about and how it continues to be tolerated. This circumstance is surely the most graphic illustration of the general suspicion that resources in the NHS are not distributed rationally. For here we appear to have gathered for relative neglect some of the relatively few conditions where we can offer the prospect of major long-term benefit following comparatively cheap treatments.

To gain an answer to these wider questions concerning waiting lists we must first look beyond resources and management. In particular the debate must be widened to acknowledge the importance, first, of the priorities set by the profession itself and, secondly, of public responses to the waiting list conditions. As was acknowledged in a *Lancet* leader. 'Many of the problems of waiting lists are behavioural' (Anonymous, 1987). 'These are the problems that will be examined in the remainder of this chapter.

THE RATIONALITY OF NHS CARE IN HISTORICAL PERSPECTIVE

It is a truism to state that hospitals have other purposes than to undertake those specialised treatments and operations which are most appropriate to the needs of the population. Nevertheless, one ideal in health care is the achievement of a rational allocation of resources. This is the concern of the health economist (see Chapter 2), whose basic conception of economic rationality is quite simple; that is, rational action consists in the efficient use of available means to ensure the maximum attainment of given ends. The health economist works with an idea of corporate rationality as a sum of idealised individual actors who have set themselves goals and are behaving in a way which would most effectively realise these goals. Indeed, rationality and efficiency are to be seen as two sides of the same coin (Ashmore *et al.*, 1989).

However, another tradition within the social sciences also attempts to address issues of rationality, especially the seeming disjunction between collective goals and individual action. Social anthropology builds upon intensive studies of small scale societies in order to derive comparative analyses of social institutions (Frankel, 1986). What may seem bizarre and indeed 'irrational' in terms of the outsider's value system can become 'rationalised' within its cultural context (Hollis, 1970:222). The point here is that the goals of rational action may well be culturally determined. At issue is not whether the capacity for rational behaviour is a universal attribute, but how to understand the goals to which it can be directed, and whether, given the variety of roles any one person has, it is possible that there are equally a variety of goals of rational action. In relation to health care systems, where the overriding concern is the equitable and efficient distribution of finite resources, it is important to understand at which point certain cultural goals take priority over others and result in behaviour that appears to conflict with the more generally accepted 'ends', such as the scheme of utilitarian advantage.

How does all this relate to the waiting list problem? It is clear that between each of the various cultures which comprise the health system, norms and shared perceptions may differ one from the other. Within each component of the health service, characteristic patterns of activity can be seen to be rational in terms of the interests and values of that professional culture, as is the case with societies studied by anthropologists. However, such rationality will not conform to any external grid of rationality, which here would be offered by the scheme of utilitarian advantage. The origins of the current irrationality of service provision can readily be sought in a brief diversion through the history of hospitals.

Hospital provision on a large scale is a fairly recent development. There was about one bed to 5000 persons in 1800 (Pinker, 1966), compared to one bed to 159 persons in 1988 (Department of Health, 1989). Hospital treatment was not seen as desirable, so that, where possible, people obtained what treatments were available at home. Many hospitals insisted that patients should be able to deposit or guarantee their funeral expenses before they could be admitted. This was to avoid such expenses falling on the hospitals' own funds, but must have functioned as an added disincentive to admission (Abel-Smith, 1964:12).

The expansion of the voluntary hospitals in the nineteenth century occurred for a number of reasons. Increasing urbanisation, as well as increasing public interest and donation were important, but the main impetus for expansion came from doctors who required hospitals to further their own interest in research and teaching (Abel-Smith, 1964:16). Once experience of hospital practice had been added to the examination requirements of the College of Surgeons and the Society of Apothecaries, the numbers of students attending hospitals increased rapidly, and hospitals responded to this demand by establishing medical schools (Newman, 1957). The collection of large numbers of cases in one building allowed comparison between patients, and furthered understanding of diagnosis and disease (Shryock, 1979). As these patients were in receipt of charity they had limited control over the provision that was offered.

Admission policy in the voluntary hospitals was gradually modified as the priorities of the profession came to dominate. The public supported the use of the charitable funds that they provided for the care and relief of chronic complaints (Abel-Smith, 1964:44–5). However, members of the medical profession were more concerned to demonstrate cures and extend their therapeutic range, and were unwilling to care for those who demonstrated the limits of their clinical powers. When St Thomas's Hospital formally excluded incurable cases, Mr Thomas Guy, one of the governors, decided to set up a second hospital specifically for incurable and mental cases. However it was not long before Guy's Hospital followed the conventional admission policy. This left only one hospital in London, the Hospital for Incurables at Putney, which did not attempt to restrict itself to acute cases. Since the middle of the nineteenth century admission policy has thus been dominated by the medical profession's interpretation of priorities, rather than by the preferences of the general population.

Thus infectious and chronic disorders, clearly the most important burdens for poor and rich alike, were effectively excluded by the prestigious institutions. Whatever contribution hospitals made in these fields was relegated to the public authorities. By 1861, in addition to 11 000 cases in voluntary hospitals, some 50 000 were under the care of workhouse medical officers (Pinker, 1966:53). The principle of less-eligibility, whereby workhouse conditions had to compare unfavourably with those of the poorest paid labourer in order to discourage malingering, rendered workhouse hospital accommodation in general extremely miserable. For example, in Cardiff Workhouse the patients led 'a life which would be like that of a vegetable were it not that they preserve the doubtful privilege of sensibility to pain and mental misery' (Lancet Sanitary Commission, 1866:vi).

The differing origins of the hospitals, as a source of clinical practice and research and as places of care for the poor sick, led to the clearly unsatisfactory situation where the public was 'lavishing princely munificence on the splendid institutions which ostensibly supply the national hospital requirements' but 'ignored the real hospitals of the land' (Lancet Sanitary Commission, 1866:ix). There thus arose two contrasting organisations for hospital care. On the one hand was that prestigious tier of medical practice, where admission policy was directed towards those conditions that accorded with the intellectual and financial interests of the medical profession. On the other was the residue, where medical officers did not have the authority to countermand the financial and other priorities of the guardians and masters of the workhouse hospitals, for here doctors were in inferior positions.

One fascinating feature of the 1948 settlement with the profession was that the rights which certain doctors had obtained, through working in voluntary hospitals on an unpaid basis, were extended to all consultants and specialists. In practice, the National Health Service became the means whereby doctors working in local authority hospitals widened their professional autonomy. As Abel-Smith (1964:499) put it: 'The doctors had asked for the best of both worlds – the full pay of the local authority hospital and the honorary status of the voluntary hospital. But, paradoxically, the nationalization of all hospitals proved to be a means of granting it.' The priorities of the medical profession have therefore continued to dominate the pattern of hospital provision. It is only now that serious attempts are being made to limit this autonomy.

MODERN PRIORITIES IN MEDICAL SERVICES

It is clear that the content of hospital services has been guided in the past by considerations other than the rational application of resources to health needs. What evidence is there that this is still the case today? The control exercised by hospital consultants over hospital admission is such that their own clinical priorities are a key influence upon treatment patterns. Such clinical priorities are crucial in setting the practices which lead to long waiting times. The mortlake of patients who wait for long periods is clearly the product of a process of selection, and is therefore an implicit expression of clinical priorities. While the public may effectively accept this, it is the profession which sets these priorities.

The waiting list conditions may be important in that they are common, but it is vital to assess how important they really do appear to the profession. Rather than just report what doctors say about these conditions, it is desirable to devise some index of professional interest in particular conditions, an index which may reflect the level of attention that each condition attracts.

Table 1.3 The index of interest in various diagnoses
(number of papers listed in Index Medicus 1986 in English
/discharges and deaths from Hospital In-patient Enquiry x 1000)

Diagnoses	Discharges and deaths	Index of interest (Papers/D & D x 1000)
Slow virus diseases of CNS	40	2000
Myasthenia Gravis	930	156
Crohn's Disease	6670	44
Carcinoma of the breast	41220	33
Rheumatoid Arthritis	26060	27
Carcinoma of the bronchus	54440	20
Myocardial infarction	102720	10
Cerebrovascular disease	111250	7.7
Irritable bowel etc.*	19840	6.7
Cataract	54990	6.5
Hip replacement	37400	5.0
Haemorrhoids	20700	1.0
Inguinal hernia	64400	0.8
Tonsils and adenoids	76600	0.7
Varicose veins	47160	0.6

* includes irritable bowel syndrome, dumping syndrome, constipation and other functional bowel disease.

One indication of professional interest is the number of scientific papers published on a particular clinical condition. The professional interest in different conditions cannot be compared without taking account of differences in prevalence. One index of medical interest is therefore the ratio of papers published on a topic to the quantity of clinical activity that it represents. Such an index (papers/discharges and deaths x 1000) is portrayed in Table 1.3 (Frankel, 1989).

Three broad kinds of conditions emerge with three broad levels of interest. First there are those conditions which may be rare, but which excite a lot of enthusiasm. Slow virus diseases reveal an index of 2000, though these conditions are not important as far as routine services are concerned. This is equivalent to two papers per episode. Then there are those conditions which, while relatively common, still attract interest, such as myocardial infarction, for example, which generates about one paper per 100 episodes. Finally there are those conditions which are common, but which do not appear to generate intellectual interest. Varicose veins here produce approximately one paper for each 2000 admissions. It is relevant that the waiting list conditions are all at the bottom of the range on this index of interest.

There are obvious limitations to this crude index. One rationalisation of this apparent lack of interest in the waiting list conditions is that all the important research has now been done. While the idea that there is little more to discover in a particular field is self-fulfilling, in these particular areas it is quite misplaced (Frankel, 1991). For example scrutiny of uncontroversial clinical activities, such as prostatectomy, has revealed major variations in practice and outcome, variations which raise basic questions about conventional practice (Roos *et al.*, 1989; Anonymous, 1989b).

The trends revealed by this index of medical interest are so gross that they cannot be dismissed out of hand. The fact that the profession may find the management of certain conditions uninteresting is an important ingredient that may give rise to long waiting times, persisting from one decade to the next.

PUBLIC RESPONSES TO THE WAITING LIST CONDITIONS

Where something supposedly unacceptable remains relatively unchanged it is important to consider wider reasons for its enduring. When looking at health services and their problems health professionals tend to look too hard for explanations within their organisation or specialty. It is a commonplace that the health systems of other societies cannot be understood adequately without considering the culture and environment where choices concerning health care are made (Frankel, 1986; Frankel and Lewis, 1989). When considering the functioning of the NHS, it is also important to look outside the organisation in order to consider whether the difficulties within could also be an expression of wider aspects of our society.

While waiting lists are indeed taken seriously by individuals outside the health service, that concern has not produced concerted and effective action. It is revealing to compare those circumstances which do produce an effective public response with those which do not. A number of circumstances seem to come together to produce effective public responses. One issue can be personal pathos, particularly involving a child. Not surprisingly, the conditions which tend to elicit public sympathy appear to be those which may cut life short in its prime. Appeals for scanners or cancer research benefit from this.

The public, in distinction to individual sufferers, does not appear to have a general interest in problems like piles, hernias and varicose veins. These are low status and private conditions which, like adenoids, may be associated in jokes and stereotypes with poverty and failure. When there is a shortfall in the provision for these sorts of conditions we do not see the concerted outcry which arises when a cardiac surgery unit is forced to close. Instead the provision of these services is effectively accepted on the terms on which they are offered, which may include waiting, or not receiving them at all. Thus relative passivity in the face of long waiting lists is first understandable in terms of the public perception of embarrassing conditions. The lack of concerted public response to the waiting list problem is mirrored in the priorities for funding identified by the various medical charities.

A second aspect of these conditions is their relationship to age. Again this taps a wider public perception concerned with expectations of ageing. The important waiting list conditions which are not in some sense embarrassing, such as hip replacements and cataract removal, are those which are intended to redress the effects of ageing. We make these available in general terms, but not in fact available to many of those who would benefit from them. Acceptance of this state of affairs accords with a public perception that clouded lenses and worn-out hips are all that can be expected in old age. The acceptance of waiting lists thus accords with perceptions of what the aged may reasonably expect from the rest of society.

Finally, in relation to the public toleration of the present form of waiting lists, we must consider the waiting culture which is the patient's view of medical treatment (Frankenberg, 1988). The surgery anteroom is known as the 'waiting room'. The relative passivity of waiting patients and the lack of effective public outcry relates to the low expectations of public provision, an attitude which has some continuity with the tradition of the Poor Laws. Access to treatment for the waiting list conditions has certain resonances with access to the Poor House. The more prosperous are able to buy these interventions, as the wealthy of the nineteenth century obtained home care. The conditions under which interventions for the waiting list conditions may be offered has some equivalence to the idea of less-eligibility (see Chapter 5). These treatments are obtained within the NHS *via* a trial by waiting. If you tolerate the wait, and do not seek a private solution to your predicament, then you are truly deserving of public relief.

These opening remarks are intended to demonstrate that the waiting list problem has many facets. Assertions of complexity can provide a pretext for inaction. Here this would be a false conclusion. The simplistic view of the waiting list as the inevitable product of a mismatch between resources and demand leads to a sterile debate that swings between fatalistic acceptance and demands for additional resources. The complexity of the waiting list phenomenon encourages a range of responses which may prove beneficial at a variety of levels within the health care system. Before proposing solutions to waiting lists, or before asserting their inevitability, it is important to establish the scope and content of the phenomenon.

In this book we are more concerned with aspects of the nature of waiting which reflect the medical culture within the NHS. Ultimately the waiting list problem must be seen as an unsatisfactory outcome of the implicit priorities of medical care in Britain. This book therefore consists largely of an excursion through each level of the health system.

CHAPTER 2

Waiting Lists and Health Policy

John Cullis

> The main question in the political economy of health services
> is the ancient one of the division of labour as between the
> individual and the state. (Lees, 1976:3)

Despite the survey popularity of the National Health Service (NHS) as
a form of public expenditure, this main question more than ever drives
much of the recent debate about health care provision. A key issue in
this debate is the waiting list for inpatient treatment, which has been
described as 'one of the largest queues in the Western world' (Lindsay
and Feigenbaum, 1984:405). The implication is that the waiting list or,
more importantly, the waiting time of potential inpatients is an evil that
attaches to state provision alone.

It is often thought or implied that state provision of health care necessarily involves waiting lists, while market provision does not, and that
waiting lists are in some sense a needless form of rationing mechanism.
This chapter contests such a view and discusses methods through which
improved 'efficiency', as regards waiting lists, may be achieved. The
issue of waiting for treatment is discussed in relation to the various
broad policy alternatives and NHS experience of waiting is placed in
the context of access to treatment, particularly surgical treatment. Some
comparisons are made with differing health care systems, especially
that of the USA, and the issue of the rational allocation of resources
is considered in the context of the current management of waiting list
conditions before an analysis of the question of a possible optimal size
and nature of waiting lists.

In the literature on the economics of health, inpatient health care is
a specialised input into the production of a fundamental commodity,
'health' (Becker, 1965; Grossman, 1972). Individuals are viewed as com-
bining inputs of all types with both positive and negative contributions
to produce their own 'chosen' level of health.

15

These introductory statements suggest two questions in relation to waiting lists. First, to what extent are they simply the product of the NHS rather than an insurance type system of health care provision? Second, how can waiting list policy best contribute to the production of 'health'?

No attempt is being made here to suggest that the only problem within the NHS is the number of people recorded as waiting. Health care is a complex good and health systems are complex forms of delivery organisation. There is a very large literature on what makes health care 'different', if anything, and the policy relevance of any differences identified (Culyer, 1983). Insurance systems are dogged by problems of moral hazard, adverse selection, incomplete coverage, and so on (see p. 24 below), whereas state type systems are often seen as vehicles to further the interests of bureaucratic monopolists, with the notion of competition a very dirty word and the interests of the consumer-patient relegated to subordinate status (see Spicer, 1982 for this type of view and suggested reforms).

The variety of health care systems observed around the world stands testimony to the lack of policy consensus in this area. All systems have imperfections, different pros and cons to be weighed. As a way of 'getting into' the two specific questions posed above it is convenient to rehearse a basic framework before probing a little deeper.

'POPULAR' MARKET V. STATE VIEWS

In the (neoclassical) economic framework waiting lists do not show up, because where quantities of any good or service demanded or supplied per period are not equal, price adjustment removes the disequilibrium. In Figure 2.1(a) if the price of inpatient health care per unit was OP1 then demand would be OMd, whilst supply would be OMs. Upward adjustment of price per unit from OP1 to OPe removes this excess demand and both demand and supply equal OMe units per period. In market contexts there are not so much shortages or surpluses, but rather self-correcting non-equilibrium prices.

Now consider Figure 2.1(b). In a state (NHS) type system, the money price of health care is frequently zero. The level of inpatient provision is government determined at OGs.[1] The curve labelled Need at OGn units is the volume of inpatient care per period accepted/dictated by specialist consultants in the NHS. There is clearly excess demand Gs – Gn. The vertical nature of need and supply curves arises because there is no relationship between them and price. (For this representation of need, see Jeffers *et al.*, 1974, and Cooper, 1975.) Given these shapes and

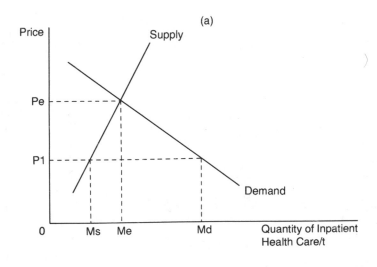

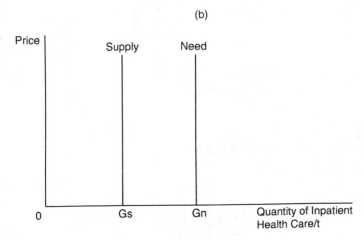

Figure 2.1 Dealing with shortages: market v. state

a money price legislated to be zero, the shortage fails to disappear through price adjustment and remains a target of criticism, especially, but not exclusively, for market advocates.

This visible 'shortage' situation is resolved in a number of ways which imply different associated costs and benefits:

(i) adjustments can be made to OGs via government provision. This option, historically, has not had the effect of closing Gs-Gn. Comparing

Table 2.1   UK NHS expenditure as proportion of Gross National Product (GNP)

Year	GNP at factor cost £b	NHS expenditure public £m	NHS expenditure patients + £m	NHS expenditure Total £m	Total NHS as % GNP	NHS cost per head £	Total NHS cost at 1949 prices* £m	Total NHS cost Index* 1949=100
1949	11.14	437		437	3.92	9	437	100
1950	11.70	477		477	4.08	10	473	108
1955	17.05	582	26	608	3.57	12	473	108
1960	22.88	866	36	902	3.94	17	583	133
1965	31.93	1 274	32	1 306	4.09	24	726	166
1970	44.53	1 979	67	2 046	4.59	37	922	211
1975	96.69	5 188	108	5 296	5.48	94	1217	278
1980	199.38	11 629	282	11 911	5.97	212	1417	324
1985	306.16	17 837	563	18 400	6.01	325	1582	362
1986e	323.66	19 181	620	19 801	6.12	350	1663	381
1987e	347.02	20 712	691	21 403	6.17	377	1732	396

Notes   All figures relate to calendar year.
+ Figures relate to NHS charges paid by patients for items such as prescription medicines, dental treatments and glasses, etc.
* Figures have been adjusted by the GDP implied deflator, at factor cost.
b = Billion (i.e. thousand million)
m = Million
e = OHE estimate(s)

Source   Office of Health Economics, Compendium of Health Statistics, 6th edition, OHE: London 1987

Table 2.2   NHS hospitals – number of in-patients on waiting list in England, 31 December ('000s)

Specialty	1955*	1960*	1965*	1970	1979	1980	1981	1982	1983	1984	1985	% Change 1970–85
Medical: Total	13	13	13	11	12	12	12	14	14	14	13	20
Surgical: Total	346	358	401	411	555	512	507	603	580	573	560	36
Other: Total	92	94	102	102	120	116	105	132	109	105	106	4
All Specialties	453	466	517	526	688	640	625	746	703	692	680	29

Notes   * Figures relate to England and Wales, otherwise to England

Source   Office of Health Economics, Compendium of Health Statistics, 6th edition, OHE: London 1987

the levels of provision on the NHS in Table 2.1 with the waiting list statistics in Table 2.2 lends support to this observation.[2] There are a number of reasons for suggesting an 'encouraged inpatient hypothesis', through which increased provision increases the numbers coming forward for treatment. This possibility is discussed further below (pp. 31).

(ii) recourse to inpatient treatment as the consultant recommended form of treatment can be reduced so that OGn moves to the left. This is a type of 'discouraged inpatient hypothesis', where the number adjudged to be in need of inpatient care is decreased. This is also discussed below (pp. 22).

(iii) potential inpatients with the necessary financial means can turn to private sector alternatives, which have always been available alongside the NHS.

(iv) the current period shortage can be ignored, on the grounds that in the next or subsequent period those who currently make up Gs-Gn will make up part of OGs, because some of OGs are inpatients called from the previous period's waiting list.

The main sections which follow are intended to modify both the no-wait view of market provision and the all-wait view of the NHS. It is argued that: the comparison based on the simple analytic outlined above is far too loaded against the state; a state system may offer the possibility of maximising health production in a way that is not mirrored in the market place; different views of whose preferences are to count are not easily reconciled and, until a view is taken, there is no accepted benchmark against which to judge the optimum waiting list.

Yet what of the 'facts' of NHS provision and the length and composition of waiting lists?

Basic data on the NHS are recorded as Table 2.1, which indicates the extent of its growth in both real terms and money outlays. Although this growth has been considerable, the numbers waiting, whilst fluctuating over time, have remained stubbornly high. It is clear from Table 2.2 that the waiting list is a surgical phenomenon. This is mainly because these are the cases that are being labelled 'cold' surgical cases (for example, hernias, varicose veins, etc.), and can therefore wait. For other specialties waiting typically is not an option, so that if inpatient treatment really is not available the next best avenue of provision must be pursued. Ignoring social science discussions on the extent to which statistical 'facts' are a product of theories employed at some point earlier along the road of analysis, the question remains as to their interpretation: 'facts' do not speak for themselves.

WAITING LIST STATISTICS

Waiting lists are the differences between two large totals: the number of individuals who have been judged to require inpatient treatment and the capacity of NHS hospitals to treat inpatients. As has been noted elsewhere (Cullis and Jones, 1985), this 'difference' figure can be likened to the Public Sector Borrowing Requirement in Mrs Thatcher's macro economic policy: a politically sensitive figure whose interpretation is not an easy matter. For example, if additional numbers added to waiting lists are exactly matched by a rise in the number of cases that can be treated, the waiting list is unchanged, but it is misleading to conclude that nothing has happened in the period.

At first sight it might suggest that the waiting list should be expressed as a proportion of total cases treated per period. Although in some circumstances this helps, there are other worries. It is the causes of movements in these totals that are required for interpretation. The assumed additional names on the waiting list above may have been a consequence of any number of factors: changing population size and structure; changing patterns of ill health within a given population; technological advance making more inpatient treatments attractive relative to non-inpatient alternatives; changed number and/or patterns of GP contact; changed referral practices by GPs (see Chapter 4); changed decision thresholds employed by consultants at first outpatient clinics, and so on.

The assumed change in the capacity to treat inpatients may also be a reflection of a myriad of causes: an increased number of available beds; more theatre time and other inputs; shorter durations of stay and increased day cases, and so on. In short, a whole host of combinations of circumstances could have produced the 'no change' situation, and identifying the role of each contributory factor is essential if any normative interpretation is to be offered.

If, for example, the shorter durations of stay postulated were 'forced,' then 'no change – things worse' might be appropriate. Similarly, if the constant waiting list was achieved against a background of relaxed decision thresholds by consultants, 'no change – things better' might be a reasonable interpretation, implicitly assuming that the capacity changes were the reflection of improvements in the level of provision, which was previously inefficiently low.

When are patients waiting? This may seem to be a question that offers an obvious answer, but there are some complicating factors. Individual patients who arrive at their GP's surgery 'on spec' may be waiting, but what of those who have an appointment and have arrived early? If a GP refers a patient to an outpatient clinic and can confirm a future appointment date now, the patient is not waiting for an appointment but is waiting for the appointment date to come around. Similarly, if, on outpatient visit, they are given an inpatient admission date, they may legitimately not be part of those on the waiting list to be called for admission.

Weaver (1981: 34) notes in the context of the health care system in Alberta, Canada, that 'a change in hospital policy regarding how far ahead bookings can be made will change the size of the waiting list'. It is the inability of hospitals to offer potential inpatient dates for their treatment which gives rise to waiting list statistics and emphasis on them, as opposed to the more important question of how long it is between being judged to require inpatient care and being called for that care. Here the assumption is that it is the NHS making the offer of inpatient care which matters, but what if the wait itself alters patients' preferences, so that on being called they fail to respond? The point is that it is waiting times which are more important than lists – the numbers notionally waiting alongside you – and these are only determined *ex-post* in a non-appointment system, that is, when individuals have been called. *Ex-ante* there is information on the numbers waiting and how long they have waited to date, but no ready information on how long they will have to wait (see the discussion of the College of Health statistics on p. 35 below).

Concentrating on the wait between outpatient clinic assessment and inpatient treatment, there are two readily available sets of data – a stock measure of the number currently waiting as at a particular date and *ex-post* data of the waiting times endured by waiting list patients actually treated. The former are routinely collected by the DoH and the latter are reported in the Hospital Inpatient Enquiry (HIPE) volumes and are based on a questionnaire sample. A further difference is that the DoH data are categorised by specialty, whilst HIPE data are by the International Classification of Diseases. Both sources are used below to give a picture of the waiting problem. However, there are a number of points concerning the accuracy of waiting list data that need to be borne in mind.

Reviews of actual waiting lists reveal that names on lists include individuals whose admission has been delayed for medical reasons (e.g. waiting for cataracts to 'ripen'); whose condition has been self correcting (for example, 'infertile' women); who have moved away; who have died (hopefully of something unrelated to the reason their name is on the list!); who do not respond to being called for treatment; or who have already been treated. Such arguments suggest that waiting list data considerably overstate the position that actually obtains (Donaldson *et al.*, 1984). The 'discouraged inpatient hypothesis' provides an antidote to this note of optimism. It can be argued that patients who have to be treated soon or not at all (those with 'high' decay rates in the terms of Lindsay and Feigenbaum, 1984) are treated in a suboptimal fashion and not ideally, as would be the case if they were inpatients. If this is a widespread effect, then there is a 'hidden waiting list', whose cost is the change in output valuation without inpatient treatment, but with the treatment regime actually adopted. Whilst Cullis and Jones (1986) offer some reasons why this effect may not be thought to be significant, they do not convince everyone.

MORE REALISTIC VIEWS OF MARKET V. STATE PROVISION

Comparisons of waiting times with those incurred in different health care delivery systems are difficult to make. Insurance-based systems notionally pay for treatment on demand. However, examining the details of the Private Patients' Plan (1984), a private health insurance scheme in the UK, provides some insight. They offer private inpatient care for those who have not been treated in an NHS hospital within six weeks, thus implying that a six week wait is not unreasonable.

In the USA, where the health care system is dominated by insurance, another dimension raises cause for concern. Green (1986:10), writing in support of moves towards making health care markets work, writes of the NHS: 'We have paid too high a price for the NHS, . . . in the routine denial of treatment to hundreds of thousands of our citizens'. In the same book, Green (1986:80) quotes studies which suggest that between 19 and 33 million Americans are uninsured, and, although this has been recognised as a problem, 'reform has not yet proved possible'. The main point in this context is that the uninsured poor especially do not have the ability to appear on waiting lists and wait for treatment.

It is these observations about 'market' versus 'state' health care provision which are elaborated below in an attempt to dispel the idea that an absence of a waiting list 'problem' signifies inpatient provision is optimal.

Market systems of health care provision have at their heart insurance mechanisms which broadly operate as follows. Ignoring the administration and other transaction costs of operation, a so-called fair insurance premium (FP) is calculated as follows. If, on striking, illness X on average requires Q units of health care which cost £C per unit to produce, and the probability of the illness per period is p, then FP is the simple product:

$$FP = p.C.Q$$
$$= p.Ex$$

where $Ex = C.Q$ and is the anticipated expenditure on a case of X.

To make matters simple, suppose $Ex = £1000$; $p = 0.01$, then $FP = £10$.

The insurance system basically works because with $p = 0.01$, 1 in 100 insured people will require treatment for X, although it is not known which individuals precisely. With 100 individuals paying a fair premium, there is £1000 to cover Ex for the one individual, on average, who is unlucky and suffers from X.

With large numbers, insurance companies use actuaries to calculate how many of each type of case to anticipate, and hence to set premiums which raise revenue to cover the expenditure accordingly. In reality, the premiums will be 'loaded' to allow for profit and other production costs. While the loading will deter some risk averse individuals from buying insurance for others the value of avoiding uncertainty will exceed the loading and insurance will be purchased. In this way resources match demand in an insurance scheme and while such schemes have problems of their own, especially in terms of insuree-induced movements in p, C and Q, waiting lists, as such, are not likely to be prominent.

A look through the indexes of Medical Care Review (1969–88), a US journal which carries both articles and synopses of other published health care work, reveals as many references to Wales as to Waiting Lists! When followed up, the 'waiting' references refer to office waiting for an appointment or to scheduling waiting, that is, the time elapsed before an appointment to see a doctor.[3]

Ignoring the possibility of a 'cover-up' on a grand scale, it is easy to assume that there is no significant waiting list issue. Hence, at first blush, it is tempting to conclude that insurance-based health care is the way to avoid waiting lists. End of story!

Table 2.3   An 'imputed' waiting list for California

Approximates		
Number of Californians	. . .	23.7 m
Implied waiting list to repeat NHS experience in England	. . .	340 000
Number of uninsured Californians	. . .	5.1 m
% of Care provided 'free'	. . .	5%
Cases Admitted California	. . .	3.3 m
Uninsured requiring admission	. . .	$5.1 \times \dfrac{3.3}{23.7} = 710\,000$
Number of cases treated free	. . .	$3.3 \times 5\% = 165\,000$
Number eligible for state schemes, paying directly causing financial difficulty or untreated	. . .	545 000
% untreated to give a comparable 'implicit' waiting list problem of NHS proportions (England)	. . .	62%

Sources   American Hospital Association Annual Survey 1987 Edition. Brown *et al.* (1987)

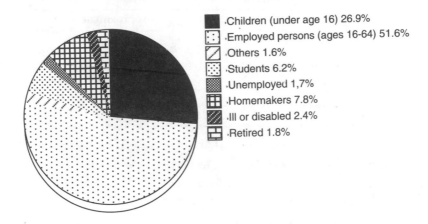

Figure 2.2   California's Medically Uninsured, 1985

However, as noted above, America may not have a visible recorded and publicised waiting list, but it does have large numbers of uninsured people. The uninsured do not have the ability to appear on a waiting list for treatment. It is not so much for many Americans that waiting times are long, but in the absence of eligibility for either the largely federal schemes of Medicare and Medicaid, state alternatives or charity, they are infinite!

The relevant question is the extent of the problem. If it is trivial, then the conclusion that insurance-based systems avoid waiting lists stands unammended. Unfortunately, such cosy evidence is missing. The uninsured represent a very significant proportion of the American population. Indeed, 'back of the envelope' arithmetic practised below gives some indication of the possible magnitudes involved. The calculation of an 'implicit' waiting list for California is illustrated as Table 2.3. The figures are culled from different sources and are by definition not ideal. However, the outcome is instructive.

Some 5.1 million Californians in 1986 had no health insurance, a 50% rise from the 3.5 million in 1979. Figure 2.2 gives a breakdown of those not insured. The surprising fact is that over half the uninsured (51.6% in 1985) are employed people between the ages of 16 and 64. As with many welfare systems, it is the working low income individuals who appear to fall through the cracks of provision. California has a population of 23.7 million, which makes it roughly half of the population of England (1985), whose waiting list figures (see Table 2.2) are employed to give the implied figure in the second row of Table 2.3. The arithmetic presented in Table 2.3 suggests that if 62% of the uninsured were ineligible for any state scheme, and/or too poor to undertake the expenses themselves, then California would have an 'implicit' waiting list of the same proportionate

Table 2.4   A change in the 'implied' US waiting list, 1979–82

	Approximates		
Population USA (1980)	226.5 m		
Admissions	33.5 m		
Average Duration of Stay	7.3 days		
Bed Days per capita	$\frac{33.5 \times 7.3}{226.5} = 1.1$ days		

	1979	*1982*	*Change*
Number poor with no insurance	12.86 m	17.54 m	4.68 m
Implied Bed Day Demand	4.68 m × 1.1	= 5.15 m	
Additional 'Free Care' (adjusted patient days)	(1980) 15.95 m	16.55 m	= 0.6 m
No. of poor patients requiring care $= \dfrac{\text{Net Implied Bed Day Demand}}{\text{Average Duration of Stay}}$		$= \dfrac{4.55}{7.1}$	= 640 000

i.e. assumes poor only have access to 'free care'. (Medicaid provision was broadly unchanged over the periods.)

Sources   American Hospital Association Annual Survey 1987 Edition. Feder *et al.* (1984)

magnitude as England in 1985. Table 2.4 offers another calculation, but this time for the whole of the USA. Feder *et al.* (1984) note how the number of poor Americans, who were either uninsured or underinsured for health care, increased during the period 1979–82. Over the same period the provision of free care in the form of explicit charity or implicit forced charity (bad debts) did not alter greatly, so that the predicted change in the number requiring inpatient care is a measure of those on an implicit waiting list, that is, not receiving care.

The precise interpretation of 'the number of poor requiring care' is ambiguous. At one extreme it would be possible to argue that, if there was no 'implicit' waiting list originally, then these changes implied the creation of one of approximately 640 000 potential inpatients. Another, more plausible, possibility is to assume there existed an implicit waiting list, comprising X numbers of names and this number represented the change in that total. For comparison purposes, the change in the numbers waiting in England over the same period was an increase of 58 000 and scaling for population differences would imply an increase of only 281 300 for the USA.

Again, it must be emphasised that these are tentative estimates, offered as a possible perspective on claims that insurance systems have no waiting list problems. The College of Health (1987:4) statement that 'long waiting lists are such a singular feature of the NHS' in context seems to imply that only in the NHS type system are there waiting lists. In a formal sense this is correct, but if the argument of this section is broadly accepted, then the statement is misleading. The crude calculations above suggest that it is reasonable to assume that the existing health care system in America has an implicit waiting list problem that is comparable with the explicit one of the NHS. That is, there are a comparable number of Americans 'in need' of inpatient care, but not currently receiving it, as in the UK, but an insurance-based system does not readily reveal these 'waiters' or their fate.

A further consideration makes the case against the insurance-based system much more damning. Whilst the waiting list in the UK is constructed on the basis of medical judgement, so that it comprises cases which can wait, for the insurance system the picture is different. Here it is individuals with all types of ill health, ranging from trivial to life threatening, who are part of the hidden or invisible implicit waiting list. 'Horror stories' picked up by the press and politicians may not be typical, but the fact remains that they are there to be reported. Insurance- based systems make people wait in relation to the distribution of income, whereas a state system tends to make people wait in relation to the distribution of ill health.

The arguments presented so far are summarised in a pictorial taxonomy as Figure 2.3 The 'wavy' outline is the set of ill individuals, with the most serious cases imagined to be at the centre and the degree of ill health reducing away from the centre. The wavy line represents the uncertain boundary between being ill and well. Illustrations (a) and (b) represent the 'stereotyped' ends of the health care provision spectrum, with (a) the market model and (b) the state model.

In the market model the waiting list is implicit in the form of the uninsured. There is also some implicit waiting in the form of insured individuals not covered for particular 'doubtful' illnesses. The black shaded areas are overprovision or 'belt and braces' medicine, depending on your viewpoint, encouraged by private insurance incentives. In panel (b) the state system has less overprovision with an explicit waiting list around the edges. It is the location of the waiting list that is a vital distinction. In the market model it appears as a 'slice', thereby including very serious and serious cases alongside less pressing ones. As argued above, a benefit of the state model is that it largely confines the waiting lists to the borders of the panel, that is to the less serious cases.

Panels (c) and (d) represent the USA and UK cases with the former being closer to (a) and the latter to (b). The introduction of a 'state' sector in the USA panel and a private sector in the UK panel does not alter the essential location of those implicitly or explicitly waiting. If the taxonomy has a cutting edge, then it should be possible to gain

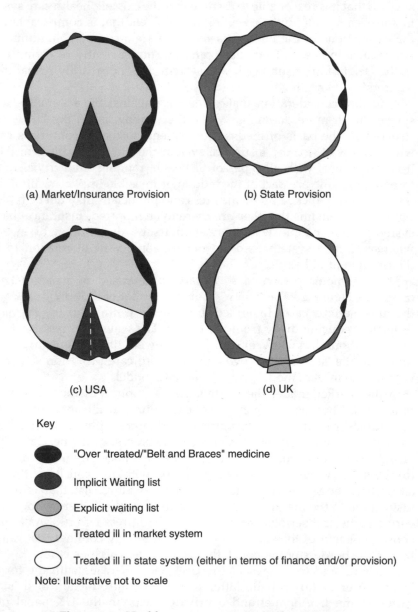

Figure 2.3   Health care systems: pictorial taxonomy

Table 2.5   Waiting lists and waiting times for Denmark

Condition	Waiting List (End of 1988)	Waiting time for treatment (Average in Months 1988)
Cataract	9217	8.2
Sterilisation (women)	3786	7.9
Hip replacement	3550	7.6
Knee surgery	2060	9.5
Varicose veins	3069	5.4

Source   Danish National Board of Health, 1989

insight into the types of problem reported in a health care system from its general description. For example, Denmark is a country with a health care system which is close to that found in the UK. It is financed through central and local government and has a small private sector. As such, explicit waiting lists for 'cold' conditions should appear as a prominent issue. In this respect it is interesting to note that since January 1987 the Danish National Board of Health has collected data on waiting lists and times for various conditions. Overall data are recorded as Table 2.5. It suggests a 'waiting' problem at least comparable with that of the NHS. Arguing that other systems of provision have an implicit or explicit problem equally as large as that in the UK may be useful in the public policy debates about health care provision, but it is a somewhat negative point to make. The real task is to look for welfare-improving policies in relation to the NHS waiting list.

MAKING THE WAITING LIST PROBLEM LESS VISIBLE OR INVISIBLE

As the other chapters in this volume testify, there is no shortage of 'good ideas' about waiting lists. In this and the next section a few past contributions are introduced. Buchanan (1965) discusses the inconsistencies of the NHS in comparison with a private market outcome. Zero user price, assuming no other costs, expands use until the value of an additional unit of health care also becomes zero. On the supply side, individuals are asked to vote for a tax contribution that effectively pays for the care of others. If individuals attach less weight to others than they do to themselves, state supply of health care resources mediated through a voting process will be less than supply, via insurance purchase, in a market context, where purchase offers direct consumption benefits to the purchaser. Hence, extensive excess demand, resulting in waiting lists that are endemic, is predicted.

Buchanan's favoured response is a return to the market, so that supply and demand sides are joined, as in the discussion above (pp. 16). In the absence of this reform he suggests that the government distribute available health services in a specific manner, either as an entitlement to a given quantity of care (Q) (for example, surgery visits, hospital days, etc.), or to a given value of care (C.Q.), where C is the cost of a unit of health care. The second option requires the costing of different types of health care provided. Given the rigorous introduction of either mechanism, supply and demand will be matched. Any demands for health services over and above that matched with public supply would be directed towards the private sector. This proposal eradicates waiting lists by almost legislating them away in the public sector and pricing them away in the private sector, which is a surface rather than a fundamental response.

Cullis and Jones (1985) similarly offer a policy which may help reduce the size of the waiting list to a target level. They argue that subsidies to waiting list patients to go private will affect the waiting list by being less sensitive to consultants' changing admission decision thresholds, which appear to follow the expansion of NHS provision. The issue here relates to the so called agency effect, or what was earlier termed the 'encouraged inpatient hypothesis' (p. 19–20). Increases in direct public expenditure or inpatient provision may cause consultants to stress the importance of inpatient treatment to all potential recipients of a particular form of inpatient care, thus in effect lowering the decision threshold of consultants with regard to admission policy.

A different response is to divert patients who would otherwise have been treated in some other way to inpatient treatment. In the former case the demand for inpatient care shifts as a whole, whilst in the latter case only those currently within the NHS fold are affected. Whichever of these responses occurs influences the attractiveness of direct public provision versus subsidies for waiting list patients to 'go private' as policy options. The authors see this as a 'number' reducing policy and are ambivalent about the welfare consequences, as these will vary with the criteria adopted. Possible evaluative criteria are discussed below, but the suggestion is that for a collective institution this should be a collective choice.

MAKING THE WAITING LIST PROBLEM VISIBLE (HEALTH OUTPUT APPROACH)

The suggestions above, whatever their merits, do not directly pose the fundamental question of what is secured in the way of output from inpatient treatment, and hence link with the production of 'health'

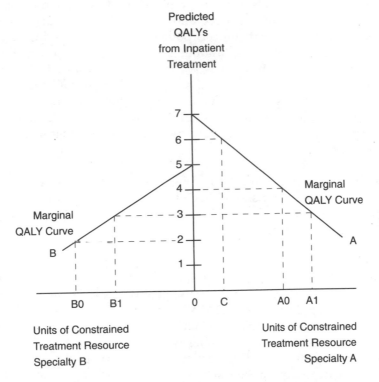

Figure 2.4   Waiting list management by QALYs

mentioned in the Introduction. Professor Alan Williams is one economist who has consistently advocated health care output measurement as a necessary pre-requisite of efficient resource allocation in the NHS.

Recently, this approach has been advocated for waiting list selection policy (Williams, 1988). The output measure combines a quality of life aspect, in terms of reduced disability and distress consequent on treatment, and a quantity aspect. The quantity aspect is measured in life expectancy in years, hence the mnemonic QALY (Quality Adjusted Life-Year). For waiting list conditions it might be expected that the quality aspect would dominate – adding 'life to your years not years to your life', as Heyink (1990) puts it.

The proposal is illustrated in Figure 2.4 Each specialty would rank the patients on its list periodically by their predicted QALY score and then select those patients who will maximise the total predicted QALYs secured. In the Figure, specialty A and B are illustrated and it is assumed that they are equally efficient in resource use. The curves labelled Marginal QALY Curves represent patients[4] ordered as suggested. The first patient for specialty A is expected to produce 7 QALYs and for specialty B, 5 QALYs. Given the resource allocation 0A0 to specialty A and 0B0 to specialty B, the marginal (last) patient treated secures 4 QALYs in A and 2 QALYs in B. Two implications are clear. First, resources should be allocated away from B towards A, because only at 0B1 for B and 0A1 for A will the additional QALYs from the last patient called for inpatient treatment be equalised at 3 and total 'output' then maximised. Secondly, the shape and location of the Marginal QALY Curve reflects the nature of the patients currently on the list and here it is worth quoting Williams (1988:240):

> A specialty with a small list of people waiting a short time for very beneficial treatment should have priority over one with a long list of patients who have been on it for ages but who will benefit very little from the treatment even when they get it.

Priority here does not, of course, mean that one specialty will always 'dominate' another except in the special case where patients are homogeneous within specialties but different between specialties, which would imply horizontal marginal QALY curves at 7 for A and 5 for B in Figure 2.4. There are benefits claimed for this approach. First, doctors have little incentive to foster long waiting lists to use as the basis for a resource claim. Secondly, there will be less use of the waiting list as a 'holding tank' for patients who may have a self-correcting condition. Whilst patients for the more beneficial inpatient procedures should have less recourse to the private sector, those expected to benefit very little would tend to find it their only option. So, for example, in Figure 2.4, if 0C resources are to be allocated, only patients from specialty A will be called. If circumstances do not change there is no chance of inpatient treatment for specialty B waiters. In the NHS individuals waiting for plastic surgery for tattoo removal are close to being in this position.

Table 2.6 offers some data, presented in Williams (1985), relating to cardiac procedures, hip replacement, kidney transplantation and kidney dialysis. Whilst the author admits that these data are crude and capable of refinement that may alter the rankings (for example, use of a wider definition of costs), it seems clear that at the margin additional resources should be directed to pace-makers for heart block as opposed to, say, hospital dialysis. Making the heroic assumption that UK QALY results were reproduced in Denmark[5] what might be inferred? The waiting time in 1988 for hip replacement was on average 7.6 months compared to 9 months for coronary by-pass operations, which on the Williams data (not shown here) had a higher cost per QALY, even for the most severe cases, thus suggesting that the ordering at least seems appropriate.

Table 2.6 Illustrative service cost per QALY data

Medical Procedure/Treatment	Present Value of Extra Service Cost per QALY Gained (£'000s)
Pacemaker implantation for artioventricular heart block	0.7
Hip replacement	0.75
Valve replacement for aortic stenosis	0.9
Kidney transplantation	3.0
Heart transplantation	5.0
Haemodialysis at home	11.0
Haemodialysis in hospital	14.0

Source Williams (1985)

The use of a physical measure of output is adequate for the internal allocation of resources between specialties, within a hospital and between hospitals, but not for comparisons with other public expenditure options. Here a monetary measure of the 'rate of return' is required for comparison. In other words, QALY information would have to be converted to monetary information. The problem here is that there are a number of bases on which this might be done. The question of the source of valuation is clearly tied up with the question of an optimal waiting list, which in general is the one that arises when the marginal benefit of the marginal patient treated per period equals the marginal cost of inpatient treatment, either in terms of expanding inpatient capacity or using existing capacity more intensively. However, before turning to this issue, what is the evidence from the current waiting list allocation policy and what are the reservations on the use of QALYs?

An implication of the Williams argument is that an efficient waiting list and time policy would exhibit a greater consistency across illnesses/specialties within districts and regions than between them. The argument is that, if data define cases sufficiently closely, they would offer similar expected health 'output', and therefore consistency of waiting times would be recommended. However, this implicitly assumes that resources corrected for 'need' are approximately equalised across regional and district health authorities. As noted above, HIPE data organised by ICD do give waiting time information, but, given these two caveats, it is difficult to draw strong conclusions.

Table 2.7 offers some data on mean and median waiting times for typical conditions on waiting lists occurring in different regional health

Table 2.7　Mean and median waiting time (weeks) for typical waiting list conditions 1985

Regional Health Authority of Residence

	Northern	York shire	Trent	East Ang- lian	North West Thames	North East Thames	South East Thames	South West Thames	Wessex	Oxford	South West- ern	West Mid- lands	Mersey	North West- ern	England NOS
Varicose veins of lower extremities															
	35.3	34.1	44.6	39.4	24.2	37.1	36.0	36.8	42.9	49.6	47.0	39.5	39.2	28.6	–
	13	16	21	26	9	20	17	10	22	21	27	20	13	14	–
Haemorrhoids															
	15.2	14.6	22.5	25.4	17.5	16.6	14.4	12.6	20.9	18.1	16.3	14.6	17.0	15.1	–
	8	8	9	7	6	10	10	8	7	6	9	7	8	5	–
Hernia of abdominal cavity															
	14.8	14.0	23.9	18.7	10.7	14.8	15.2	14.3	18.4	21.5	19.0	23.1	28.4	15.8	7.1
	8	8	10	10	5	8	9	7	10	8	9	10	8	7	7

Source　Hospital In-patient Enquiry (1988)

Table 2.8 'Non-urgent' waiting in England and Wales (Sept. 1986)

Specialty	Total waiting	Total non-urgent	% non-urgent waiting over 1 year
1. General surgery	155 061	145 245	25% *
2. Trauma&orthopaedics	143 237	129 587	33%
3. Ear, nose & throat	112 186	107 532	23%
4. Gynaecology	97 083	92 708	14%
5. Ophthalmology	57 897	56 167	17%
6. Oral surgery	50 365	48 543	30%
7. Plastic surgery	37 282	35 082	51%
8. Urology	35 079	29 186	20%
Total	688 190	644 050	26%

* These figures include urology total for Wales

Source College of Health, Guide to Hospital Waiting Lists 1987, College of Health: London, 1987

authorities in 1985. Variation is considerable and median waiting time probably less than is commonly assumed.

Against this background it can be seen that the College of Health's efforts to equalise waits is unattractive because it is equalising waits about the health output maximising values that matters, not equalising waits *per se*. Indeed, the College seems, as a first target, to want to have the government guidelines on waiting lists enacted, which, in this context, may be mistaken. The guidelines are that no one should wait more than three months for a first outpatient clinic appointment; one month for urgent inpatient admission; twelve months for non-urgent inpatient admission.

Table 2.8 indicates the 'margin' by which the last target is missed. The latter two categories are based essentially on the rate of deterioration of the potential inpatient. To the extent that this correlates with predicted QALY output, conflict of criteria will be lessened. However, a blanket time for all patients does not make sense in a Williams' framework, where 'equal marginal output', irrespective of past wait, is the rule. Here there may be some conflict over notions of efficiency and equity. Whilst output maximisation at first sight seems attractive, it is far from unassailable. The re-ranking envisaged will always leave those with low expected output beyond the pale, however long they have waited. This may grate to the extent that, normally, a long enough wait ensures arrival at the head of the queue. Hence in most/all waiting list formulae, 'time on the list' is an argument (which in itself is likely to lengthen lists).

For example, Culyer and Cullis (1976) suggest a formula based on the following criteria:

(i) time already spent on the waiting list;
(ii) urgency based on the expected rate of deterioration of the patient's condition;
(iii) urgency based on the patient's health status;
(iv) urgency based upon the 'social productivity' of the patient and the number of economic dependants;
(v) urgency based upon other social factors.

Williams' discussion of the 'ho hum lets wait and see' patients on the list seems to relate implicitly to criterion (i), that is, that these patients should not be on the list. At minimum this creates a transitional problem of those who are currently on the list in the expectation of treatment. Also, it indicates that information should be readily available on what can or cannot be expected. The plastic surgery example above would be a case where people's expectations may be unrealistic.

Broome (1987) has gone furthest in exposing QALYs to detailed examination, especially at the philosophical level. First he emphasises the equity point above, and in so doing offers a reason for 'time on the list' being a relevant consideration. He argues that QALYs are about assessing the 'total of good' and as such do not deal with fairness, or the 'claims' individuals have. Claims are identified with duties owed to an individual and should be met in proportion to their strength and never completely overridden. Those wanting tattoo removals may be seen as having a weak claim on resources, but they should nevertheless get their share if fairness is part of what the NHS is meant to achieve. A formula that incorporates 'time on the list' as a factor is one mechanism that will eventually allow those with weak claims to be called for treatment. This may be at odds with QALY maximisation, but the argument is that such a maximising calculus is not the only criterion to be adopted in the allocation of inpatient health care.

As regards QALYs as a measure of good, Broome (1987) also has a number of reservations that lead him to conclude they are fundamentally flawed: (a) QALYs of one individual cannot be added to those of another individual unless you assume they represent the same thing to each individual. Given that individuals will differ in their 'other' than QALY characteristics, this is implausible; (b) there are philosophical and practical difficulties in basing the quality adjustment factors on individual preferences; (c) there are problems with the relevant population over which the good is to be assessed.

This last consideration Broome sees as 'most serious'. QALYs arise both by enabling new individuals to join the population (for example, infertility and ante natal care) and by extending the lives of those currently part of the population (who themselves may have more children than would have otherwise been the case). Where is the line to be drawn in measuring

QALYs? If the good of those born, who would otherwise not have been, is counted, the QALY count for 'baby making' care would tend to swamp that for extending existing lives. If the good of those who currently exist, or would exist, independent of the current decision, is counted alone, much turns on establishing a point of existence. The QALY score for a three month old baby will probably be greater than that of a thirty year old simply because of the differential life expectancy, and would therefore support resources going to the newborn before adults. Yet what if the choice is between a three month old fetus and the thirty year old adult? In addition, if it was known that the parents would have another 'replacement' baby if the fetus died, this piece of information on the second view of what constitutes the relevant population would be irrelevant.

Broome (1987) suggests a complicated discounting mechanism, justified by reference to the 'psychological connections' between successive periods in an individual's life being weaker the more periods are temporally separated, as a way out of the 'baby saving' bias. However, considering only the existing, and those who will exist, independent of the decision to be made, raises other difficulties reported by Broome. There may be 'transitivity' problems. If there are three choices, 1, 2 and 3, the decision between 1 and 2, 1 and 3 and 3 and 2 will depend on those existing in each choice pair, and there is no reason to suppose that these will comprise the same sets of individuals. Option 1 may be better than 2, 2 better than 3 and 3 better than 1, so the outcome is not unique.

A second damning consideration is what QALYs will not count. If a medical technique effectively replaces an individual disabled at birth with a healthy individual at birth,[6] most would want to count this as good. However, the healthy individual would not have otherwise existed, and would then be irrelevant as regards QALY counting.

Carr-Hill (1989) also adds to the doubt about the extensive use of QALYs as such. He highlights problems associated with the measurement and valuation of morbidity, the scaling of it and the impact of risk on the argument.

Whilst there are many other points to be made and evaluated, enough has been said to establish the view that QALYs are never likely to be far from controversy. Even if agreement could be reached on the measurement of health output, there are different arguments relating to the role that such information should play in defining 'optimal' waiting lists.

'OPTIMAL' WAITING LISTS

An economic perspective on policy prescriptions counsels caution in accepting the view of the various advocates of any position. What is often prefaced with the words 'The fact is . . . ' would more often be more accurately described as 'My value judgement is . . . .'. In particular the 'public choice' economists pose the question: 'What is in it for the advocates?'

Less cynically, there is much scope for dispute because individuals have different 'assumptive worlds' in which they interpret events. As regards the specific question of a waiting list that generates optimal waits, Table 2.9 offers a simple taxonomy of some possibilities. Different criteria will affect both the optimal waiting times as well as the mix of patients that comprise any list. The idea is to read down column (a) and pick a view of the world consistent with your view on health care judgements. Columns (b) and (c) label each approach and offer a source of information on the valuations respectively. The difference between implicit and explicit in rows II to IV amounts to the difference between 'actions' and 'words'. (In the popular version each of the approaches rests on investigating the valuations embedded in decisions made and carried out. An explicit version of each of the approaches records the statements or 'official line' of the selected decision maker.)

Clearly there may be influences of one view on another (for example, government views may be influenced by those of the medical profession etc.), but the taxonomy does help fix ideas. Some examples may help illustrate the importance of the distinctions. Row (a) is often viewed by the person in the street as a purely 'economic' view and indeed is often aped by non-economists, who, ironically, end up being more 'Catholic than the Pope'. Whilst economists in many instances are attracted to the easy quantification offered by a market production approach, the economic framework is generally seen as being about individual choice making. Individuals do not only count those things that take place on the market, and, neither, as a consequence, does the economic framework. Waiting list patients who are not currently part of the active labour force are not to be ignored.

It is row IV(a) that most closely corresponds to a standard economist's position. Here it is 'willingness to pay' that demonstrates the significance of something to an individual. In particular, the implied valuations are thought more reliable as both questionnaires and experimental approaches are inevitably hypothetical. In the analysis of actual behaviour people have placed their money where their mouth may or may not have been, to put the point rather crudely. This of course raises the question of income distribution. The valuations elicited from behaviour reflect both individual preferences and their ability to back them, that is, the prevailing income distribution. Patients' willingness to 'go private' to avoid waiting offers a source of information on the burden waiting lists impose on individuals, and Cullis and Jones (1986) have

Table 2.9 Approaches to defining an optimum waiting list

	View of World (a)	Approach (b)	Sources of information (c)
I	Maximising Gross National Product	Livelihood/(narrow) human capital	Lost market output as measured by (gross) labour earnings
II	Government sovereignty – 'merit want' view of world in which 'others' may be a better judge of an individual's welfare (or individuals delegate their choice)	(a) Implicit politico-administrative decisions	Analysis of past decisions of government
		(b) Explicit politico-administrative decisions	Statements of government policy on waiting lists
III	Producer sovereignty – the experts who produce health care are best judges of individual welfare in health care	(a) Implicit medical decisions	Analysis of waiting list management by consultants
		(b) Explicit medical decisions	Statements of medical professions (interest groups) on waiting lists
IV	Consumer sovereignty – the individual is the best judge of his own welfare (and income distribution not inequitable)	(a) Implicit willingness to pay	Analysis of individual behaviour e.g. seeking private care at a price
		(b) Explicit willingness to pay	Statements of individuals in questionnaires or experiments to elicit their views

made a calculation along these lines in the context of a specific economic model of waiting lists developed by Lindsay and Feigenbaum (1984).

Many commentators who are not smitten by the apparent unsubtleness or other perceived limitations of the economic approach, especially in relation to health care, opt for a government or producer sovereignty approach. After all, the argument might run, is the government not elected partly to be responsible and accountable for a state health care system like the NHS? As regards explicit government sovereignty, the government does provide guidelines as to the optimum waiting times. However, from an implicit viewpoint, if it is accepted that waiting times will actually respond to more resources, the government does not provide the inputs to realise their objectives. Producer sovereignty, as represented by medical expert views, makes most sense in a world where medical care is viewed as a purely technical issue not open to lay opinion.

This view is not easy to accept in a system financed by the general taxpayer. In a collectively financed system the waiting list policy might be expected to have a collective content. However, without a resolution of the question as to whose preferences are to matter and how they are to be articulated, it is difficult to go further on the question of an optimum waiting list. Different 'views of the world' imply different answers.

SUMMARY AND CONCLUSIONS

This chapter has explored a number of themes central to understanding waiting lists and waiting list policy. At one level of economic analysis they are a demonstration of the inefficiency of non-market forms of resource allocation. The argument presented here is that market orientated systems simply make waiting lists invisible, either via price rises for health care, or, more realistically, by individuals who lack health care insurance cover being unable to register a claim on health care resources. An analysis of the 'implicit' waiting list in the USA suggests that they have a problem of comparable magnitude. As evidence on the perennial 'market v state' argument in the provision of welfare type services, the existence of a long visible NHS waiting list is not a decisive one. Concerns about the quality and the interpretation of the statistics in themselves reinforce the view that they are not an easy sword to wield in any context.

The more positive aspect of this chapter centres more directly on the principles by which waiting lists might be managed and evaluated. Discussion of QALYs as a way forward offered only 'two cheers' for their introduction and consistent application. There are concerns about them at the philosophical and practical level that may or may not be resolvable in the future. In the final substantive section of the chapter the awkward question of an appropriate source of valuation is raised. Individuals trained in different disciplines tend to feel they have the 'natural' or obvious handle on the problem. Whilst economics offers (implicit) individual valuations as their natural benchmark, this does not always command wide assent in the health care arena.

However, without a resolution of the question of the yardstick by which the costs and benefits of the delay of inpatient treatment is to be measured, the further question of what is the optimal waiting list or time for the NHS to aim for is left unanswerable. Suggestions for waiting list policy that make sense by reference to one set of criteria do not necessarily make sense by reference to another. Hence the onus is on advocates for policy changes to make clear their underlying assumptions and subsequent analysis.

NOTES

Anne Jamieson provided helpful comments in general and translated the material on Denmark.

1. OGs has been made identical with OMe to abstract from 'level of provision' issues in market v state comparisons at this stage. Whether OGs is likely to be greater or less than OMe is a matter of dispute in the literature on public provision.
2. Recent data on NHS waiting lists helps illustrate this phenomenon. The former Social Services Secretary, Norman Fowler, put in £30 million in an attempt to reduce NHS waiting lists by 100 000 names over the period September 1987 to March 1988. Unfortunately over that period lists lengthened from 690 000 to 704 000, a rise of 1.9%. Only three regions, S.E. Thames, S.W. Thames and West Midlands reported a decline (see *The Observer*, 9 October 1988).
3. Correspondence with the American Medical Association indicates waiting time data are not routinely collected.
4. If treatments are divisible then the same type of approach should be applied at that margin as well.
5. The degree of heroism can be gauged from Drummond (1991) and Mooney and Olsen (1991). These authors discuss the limitations and measurement problems associated with QALYs.
6. Broome notes that some form of selection already exists in the shape of in vitro fertilization.

CHAPTER 3

Joining the Queue: Demand and Decision-making

Robert West

This chapter first discusses queuing theory, briefly reviewing some of the features of queues and of rational behaviour of people with respect to queues. Many features of queuing apply and many aspects of queuing theory are relevant to our understanding of waiting for treatment in the health service. Rational behaviour among health service waiters and rational management of health service waiting can only be achieved with relevant knowledge. Since queues arise from need, perceived need or demand for a service, it is necessary to consider these. To this end, this chapter examines the morbidity of potential patients, the amount, nature and degree of illness or disability in those who seek medical attention and considers various measures of health status. Next the benefits of medical intervention are reviewed, including the ways that the benefit may be assessed. Finally, there is a brief discussion of the economic balance, in which the pressures of pools of morbidity of potential patients with different ailments are balanced by the provision of services to meet and treat.

Before examining the issues of queuing and of how problems in queuing strategy and queue management can be solved, it is wise to consider the size of the problem. Although discussed in other chapters, it should be appreciated that the problem waiting lists are principally for relatively few clinical conditions. While the total number of patients waiting at any one time in England and Wales exceeds 500,000, when this huge number is expressed as a fraction of total hospital activity or throughput it represents merely six weeks of work. The fact that waiting for hospital treatment is seen as a problem lies largely in the fact that this rather small proportion of the total hospital throughput waits rather longer than six weeks, or in other words, that these patients bear more than their fair share of the burden of waiting.

QUEUING THEORY

Queuing theory is a well developed area of applied statistics (Cox and Smith, 1961; Lee, 1966; Cross and Harris, 1974; Winston 1987). In recent years operational research has done much to improve the efficient flow of materials in industry, of vehicles in transport and of people in banks and supermarket checkouts. In many applications operational research has examined the queue, or the bottleneck, and dissected it into its component parts, has studied in each part the arrival patterns in time and the distribution of server times to make recommendations about levels of staffing or stocking of machine parts to meet the demands made on the service. Clear analysis of queuing leads to efficient solutions which satisfy the demands, for example, by shoppers in a supermarket checkout, for a proportion of the total working week deemed acceptable by management with the minimum staff in the checkout/cashier rota.

The simplest possible queuing situation with a uniform constant rate of new arrivals and a uniform constant service time is so unreal that we should pass over it very briefly: if the arrival rate (per unit of time) is less than the service rate (per unit of time) there is no queue and the server enjoys a period of rest between each new arrival, but if the arrival rate is greater than the service time the server steadily loses ground and a queue steadily develops – to infinity! The simplest queue that is worth discussing and analysing is the single orderly queue with a single server, in which there is a variable but average interval between new arrivals and a variable but average rate of service by the single server. Here again if the average arrival rate exceeds the average server rate the queue will develop and grow *ad infinitum*.

Far and away the most common simple queuing situation involves the single server with an average rate that beats the average arrival rate, yet queues may develop from time to time. This is common experience, as, for example, in the pharmacy/chemist shop where one can normally expect to be served on entering. Nevertheless, on occasions one might arrive soon after someone else and might have to wait a few moments while that person's business is concluded. Again, on even rarer occasions, one might arrive after someone, who is negotiating some unusually long and complicated business. Because their service time is atypically long, a queue forms even if arrivals are well spaced. Many may not realise that queues may develop even when the average arrival rate is slower than the average server rate, until they reflect more deeply on their own experiences, as in the above example.

In statistical terms the queue develops when the randomly variable arrivals cluster, when the randomly variable server time for a customer, or for a sequence of customers, is longer than average or, particularly, when both arrivals cluster and longer than average service times coincide.

With knowledge of both the distribution of arrival times (usually fitted to a Poisson distribution) and the distribution of server times (often fitted to the exponential distribution), the statistician can calculate both the probability that any new arrival will have to wait and the average waiting time.

The reader will appreciate that in most real life situations people do not arrive as a random Poisson distribution. Although arrivals may not be directly related, arrivals are likely to be influenced by relatively few extraneous or environmental factors that effect a number of potential customers in a common manner. Thus, although the probability of a wait is small, when the average arrival rate is considerably lower than the average server rate and arrivals and services both follow Poisson probability distributions, the likelihood of a wait may be considerably higher if one shops at a busy time. While the postmistress in the village post office may be quite idle for parts of the day, she might be quite rushed at other times. This of course naturally leads to more complicated queuing models, where provision is adjusted to some degree to match the expected demand.

The queuing so far described is a single admissions, single server and orderly (i.e. first come first served) queue. Few queues are so simple. Many queues that we encounter in larger pharmacies/chemist shops, main post offices, supermarket checkouts and at motorway bridge tollbooths operate as a set of single admission, single server and orderly queues in parallel. The next arrivals to the whole system have a choice as to which of the queues they wish to join. Their decision is likely to take account of some knowledge or judgement regarding the options available. Assuming that their principal concern is to be served as quickly as possible, their first choice is likely to be on the basis of the length of the queues, preferring the shortest. Other information may influence their judgement of which queue is likely to move faster. In the supermarket checkout, they may rate two adjacent queues, each with the same number of waiting customers, on the basis of the size of the grocery baskets, assuming that the smaller baskets will mean quicker service times. Displayed guidance may lead them to a quick service till, for instance to 'six items or less, cash only', if the classification is appropriate to their needs. Special knowledge may also suggest a preference, like recognition that one cashier is unusually quick fingered and normally serves three customers in the time of an average two. It is clear that a rational decision, of which queue to join in order to minimise delay, depends on knowledge, even if limited and quite simple knowledge.

The next type of fragmentation to consider is the serial queue. Many queuing situations really comprise a string of individual single entry, single server queues in a row, one after the other. This can be a feature of outpatient organisation, when it may be well known that patients are block booked for 9.00 AM, but on a first come first served basis they go the rounds from clinician to nurse, to radiology and back again to clinician. Probably the most common example of this type of queuing is in the cafeteria, where one queues first for the tray, secondly for soup, next for the main course, salad or snack and in turn for sweet, coffee and pay desk. Because of the variable nature of individual selections, some taking longer to decide over the choice of soup, others over main course and others waiting for a vegetable that has just run out and needs replacing from the kitchen, the delay at any one point in time occurs at different points in the overall line. The net effect is that the flow of customers through the line and out towards their chosen tables to eat their dinners appears restricted and to be slower than it might be, yet at the same time there may appear to be servers who are not wholly occupied. Many cafeterias keep their potential diners in a line. Our own hospital cafeteria learned something from operational research or queuing theory in a recent redesign, when it clearly fragmented the sub-queues into salad bar, hot foods, sandwiches, cheese board, snacks, deserts and so on, and then further separated the pay desks from the other areas. The traditional hospital canteen lunch time queue was dramatically cut.

All the foregoing still assumes orderly behaviour in queues or sub-queues, first come first served within a queue or sub-queue, unlike when elbowing for drinks at a bar in the UK, or getting onto a bus or train in Greece. Queuing strategy, if it might be so termed, in the disorderly queue is clearly different from queuing strategy in deciding which orderly sub-queue to join, but there are common elements. In the scrum for the bar the thirsty would-be-drinker is likely to make the same sort of estimates of numbers waiting, serving rates and likely order lengths as in the supermarket checkout. In the jostle for a Greek holiday bus, or for a compartment on a continental train, a little information, such as where on the platform the emptier carriages will arrive, facilitates advantageous preparation.

Most of the foregoing assumes that the customers seek only to minimise their waiting time, but the last illustration brings up another important aspect in the choice of which sub-queue to join and that is consideration of the nature of the service when it comes. It may not be in the timetable, but nonetheless known to the cognoscenti, that there is a relief bus, on which there will be many empty seats, following the scheduled bus, which offers standing room only, unless one is very sharp in the queue barging. This becomes more significant when we move on to consider queuing within a health service: waiting time, while important, is not the only criterion for deciding which sub-queue to join.

Two main points are clearly relevant to all queuing situations. First, that the manager has options in analysing the queue, factorising the queue into its constituent part queues, identifying constraints and designing improvements to overcome the bottlenecks. Secondly, individual customers need information to decide logically about their queuing strategy; they need to know the rules of that particular queue and they need to know the facts of the queue, the lengths and the rates of flow of the constituent parts.

QUEUING IN THE HEALTH SERVICE

Just as there are many queuing situations in modern life in the Western world, there are many queuing situations within the health care business. There are waits for almost all services: for the general practitioner, dentist, chiropodist, outpatient consultation, hospital inpatient treatment and, within the hospital, for diagnostic services. Some of the waits are short- term physical queues, as in the pharmacy/chemist shop, the accident and emergency unit at hospital and in the general practitioner's traditional surgery hour, although many general practitioners have moved over the last few years towards an appointments system.

Most of the emphasis in this book is directed at the invisible, although very real, long-term queues that lie behind the appointments system for hospital outpatient consultation and hospital inpatient treatment. We are not so much concerned about the wait in minutes or hours, having presented in the clinic in the sort of queues that have illustrated the queuing theory section above, but more about the wait in weeks or months or years for specialist consultation or treatment, after the general practitioner has identified that there is a medical problem.

The principal difference, therefore, between the queuing situations with which we are mostly all too familiar in supermarkets, in banks and in transport, and the main problem queues of the health service, is that the queues are 'invisible' to the patient (or client). Consider a typical patient with a hernia. He has suspected something for several years but he only consulted his general practitioner about the problem when it got considerably worse moving furniture with his daughter and son-in-law. His general practitioner advises surgery (subject, of course, to the specialist opinion of the surgeon) and makes an appointment for the patient at his local district general hospital for a general surgery outpatient clinic. There may be some discussion between patient and general practitioner about which surgeon to see and, possibly, about which surgeon is believed to have the shortest list. There may even be some 'shopping about' done by the general practitioner on behalf of the patient, with respect to the current state of surgical waiting lists.

That would be unusual. The patient usually comes away with the impression that he is on the list for an operation, little realising that there are really four lists for three surgeons, three named and one departmental; that each list has a fast stream and a slow stream, for urgent and non-urgent patients respectively; that each list comprises two sequential queues for outpatient consultation and for inpatient treatment; and that patients may switch between streams between courses, that is they may be urgent as an outpatient and, after an examination, non-urgent as an inpatient.

The patient may also be unaware that he is eligible to join the queue at another general hospital in the same district, where the waiting list is shorter, or even that he may go elsewhere on the National Health Service to another hospital in another district (College of Health, 1987). He is probably aware that there is a private option, but it may well not have been pointed out that for many years there has been a queue-jumping option by taking one private consultation, which can move, and very often has moved, a patient from a slow stream to a fast stream in the same hospital and from the first of the sequential queues for outpatient consultation to the second for inpatient treatment.

The detail of the system, the variety of the rules under which the waiting game is played and the detail of the current situation may be too much for the patient to appreciate fully, but it is only with this knowledge that he can make his choice wisely. He may have heard that one surgeon is good, without being advised that, because many general practitioners recommend the same surgeon, that waiting list is two years longer than the other surgeon's, or that, by joining the 'departmental' list, he is likely to be seen within a month, with a 1 in 3 chance of being seen by the preferred surgeon.

For many years the outpatients waiting list has traditionally been a stack of cards or patient referral proforma in a drawer in a records clerk's office. It not only operated like a 'black box' from the patients' point of view, in that they have been ignorant of the rules of its state and of its dynamics, the waiting list has almost literally operated as a black box, in that no one has really known quite how individual cards have moved between referral and appointment. Many surgeons have given the waiting list clerks or the outpatient booking clerks a set of rules by which to order the list or to draw up a clinic, but frequently the rules are not followed to the letter. A feature of the process of referral to the list which appears to be generally unappreciated is that what is nominally still a letter of referral from a doctor (general practitioner) to a doctor (the specialist) is very rarely treated as such, and is all too often not even seen by the specialist until the patient sits in the outpatient clinic (see also Farrow and Jewell in Chapter 4).

Re-sequencing of the queue is almost universal when it comes to selection of patients for operation. The operation list for a particular day is often selected about one week in advance from the queue, taking into account a number of criteria, including case mix for variety, to satisfy a registrar's training requirements or research interest, to fit with the theatre and staff availability, as well as urgency and the time the individual patients have been in the queue. Final selection at relatively short notice unsurprisingly results in some patients being unavailable or unfit for operation, particularly if they have had long waits (Frankel *et al.*, 1989).

The 'black box' approach to waiting list management leads to inefficiencies from the service providers' point of view, as well as leaving waiting patients confused as to how to optimise their queuing strategy or simply downright ignorant of their probable waiting expectation.

In my first study of waiting in a sample of specialties in a sample of hospitals in 1970, one general surgery waiting list that turned up in the sample was interesting (West, 1970). Two surgeons sharing the same resources (outpatient clinic, theatre, wards and staff) operated under totally opposing philosophies. One sought to minimise his inpatient list, since he considered that when he had assessed a patient as needing an operation he wished that operation completed and also he knew as much as he was likely ever to know of the patient's current fitness for operation. The other sought to minimise his outpatient list, since he argued that any unassessed patient (meaning unexamined by a specialist) could be seriously and urgently in need of operation and he was prepared to accept that the majority of patients who had been assessed in his clinic could wait for operation without serious consequences. If each managed his list separately, and if all referring general practitioners in the area knew the rules and the outpatient and inpatient waiting times for each, the referring general practitioners, having made their own assessments of the condition and urgency, could have chosen fairly rationally between the two. However, with only partial information and with hospital management encouraging patients to join the shorter outpatient list, the system clogged up.

NEED AND DEMAND FOR HEALTH CARE

In the foregoing examples of queuing the need for the service and, hence, to queue, has been assumed. On reflection it will be appreciated that in many situations customers do not consider the service essential (at that time anyway) and information about the current state of the queue will often lead them to give up seeking the service, or at least to postpone seeking the service and to consider returning on another occasion, when they think the queue may be shorter or when they find that they really do need the service. Thus the customers' perceived need for the service is often influenced by the queue length, with those who consider themselves in greater need being more prepared to wait.

Need for health care is not easy to judge, particularly for the non-urgent conditions that contribute most significantly to the NHS waiting problem (see Chapter 1). The condition may cause some pain, without being intolerable, and may cause some limitation of activity, without preventing essential activities of daily living. A further aspect of need which is relevant to the patients' decision to join a non-urgent waiting list is the benefit that they may expect from the service, when they get it. The rational decision to join the waiting list depends not only on the length of the queue and the severity of the disability, but also on the improvement that medical or surgical intervention can be reasonably expected to offer, or on the improvements that the patients have been led to expect.

Once more it is clear that knowledge is necessary for rational decisions. Despite the problems that surround the definition of need for health care, any discussion of waiting for health care and of rationing and rationality in the delivery of health care should attempt to consider the issue. A queue for a service is the consequence of demand, which is a result of perceived need, which in turn should be related to actual need.

There are two potentially opposing views with regard to the demand for health care. One is that there is a finite pool of morbidity, that can be mopped up when treated by adequately and appropriately provided services. The other is that there is an infinite potential demand; that once one ailment is satisfactorily treated, the patient identifies the next less troublesome bodily malfunction and seeks repair of or treatment for that, in a constant search for the impossibly elusive state of perfect bodily and mental health. The former has been attributed frequently to the founding fathers of the NHS (for example, Cooper, 1975:25) and the latter is somewhat implicit in the current WHO definition of health (WHO, 1978). Both are untenable extremes; the reality must lie somewhere between.

The pool of morbidity theory has been disproved, if anything is ever disproved, by the very history of the NHS. Provision has grown and throughput has grown and, since waiting lists have not yet vanished

(*British Medical Journal*, 1984), it can be inferred that new morbidity has been and is still being uncovered. The infinite demand theory can be discounted by *reductio ad absurdum*. It would not be possible for us all to spend all day every day in a dentist's chair, a GP's consulting room, a hospital clinic or theatre (even if robots did all the treating), because we would still have to spend some of our time and energy on primary production activities (producing food), on secondary production (making machines) and on other tertiary production activities (like education).

Dr Halfdan Mahler, as director of WHO, clearly described the priorities given by third world countries to these important activities and often surprised listeners by ranking health as a lowly eighth or tenth. These rankings are not exclusive to the third world, since they are implicit in the proportions of gross domestic product (GDP) spent in the same basic areas in the more affluent developed countries. Even in the UK agriculture is the most important activity of man, because man needs food – daily. It is only because of increased efficiency in primary and secondary production and because of the increased use of machines and robots in the developed world that we can increase the proportion of GDP directed to the health maintenance industry. Because health care has grown in many countries through 5 and 6% towards 10 or 11%, this does not in any way indicate that growth will continue unabated and demand for health care increase indefinitely. There will continue to be greater demand for primary production.

The second reason why the infinite demand theory is untenable is that we would not wish to spend all day every day seeking health care, even if we had this choice. We only seek improved health in order to pursue some other activity or to enjoy other pursuits, be they playing football or going to the theatre. We seek health care not because we seek health *per se*, but in order to enjoy life better. Consequently, with neither the ability nor the desire to pursue health care *ad nauseam*, demand for health care is not infinite. It would be interesting to speculate about what proportion of GDP the health care industry might be expected to saturate. One pointer is that in the USA, where 11% is spent on health care, there appears to be little unmet demand in the form of waiting, though there may be unmet need among the uninsured (see Chapter 2).

If we accept that demand for health care is neither satiable by curing all illnesses, nor infinite because of other calls on man's interest and time, we should nevertheless consider what drives demand. Pursuing the rationality argument would lead us to conclude that demand should arise from need; it would be whimsical to demand treatment, if one were not ill. Although pursuing that argument too far could lead to an involved discussion of the psychosomatic and the psychiatric, its consideration at the simpler and more practical level would strongly imply that the patient with a diagnosed illness, for which there is a recognised and effective treatment, needs that treatment.

The need for the more dramatic remedies for the more traumatic conditions is not controversial: lives can be saved by surgeons in accident and emergency departments by early defibrillation when the heart stops, by thrombolysis in myocardial infarction, by penicillin for meningococcal meningitis, and so on. Likewise, certain disabilities may be resolved and some pains may be relieved, although often only for relatively brief periods. However, for the most part, medical and surgical consultations and interventions yield less clear-cut improvements or benefits. It is this 'greyness' of the benefit which results from many health care consultations or procedures that turns 'actual need', which is probably an unquantifiable concept, into perceived need.

Uncertainty as to prognosis and the potential benefit of a successful health care intervention arises both from medical (or scientific) ignorance and from patient (or individual) ignorance. In the former, it is well recognised that patients show differential response to a specific treatment, and for many conditions and for many interventions, the prognostic indicators are not fully understood. With respect to the latter, patient ignorance may be general or specific. Although the benefit of certain interventions, like the success of hip replacement, may be relatively well known to the lay public, individual patients may still be unclear as to whether their pain and limited mobility is or is not a treatable hip. Even within the system, after consultation with both GP and specialist, patients are faced with a personal dilemma because they must balance benefits with costs, each with its attendant probability estimates.

We suspect that many patients are woefully ignorant of the degree of improvement that they may reasonably expect from the service for which they are waiting. Furthermore, a significant proportion of patients on long waiting lists, despite clearly suffering some recognised medical or physical problem, may unfortunately benefit little from specialist intervention. In a study of a long orthopaedic outpatient waiting list, it was estimated that as many as one third were patients who had previously received specialist treatment and for whom further improvement was unrealistic (West and McKibbin, 1982).

While need arises if patients have an illness for which there is a recognised and effective treatment, perceived need arises when patients believe they have an illness for which they believe there is a recognised treatment and an expected benefit. Accordingly, perceived need depends, to a certain extent, on knowledge of what illnesses and conditions are amenable to treatment. There is, however, another way into perceived need, when a person, who is driven to despair by, for example, chronic back pain, will seek help from those who may know something or who may be able to do something; the desperate 'will try anything'.

Epidemiology can offer a methodology by which perceived need could in theory be quantified, by representative sample surveys of prevalence for the chronic conditions and of incidence for the acute conditions. While many such studies have been undertaken, it may seem curious that health care planners and health service managers still frequently resort to measures of use (or throughput) and of unmet demand (or waiting lists) as proxies for need. Prevalence and incidence of certain physical conditions, like cleft palate, blindness, fractured neck of femur or cancer of the stomach, are theoretically relatively easy to measure, because the diagnostic criteria are relatively unambiguous. However, for many more, like presbiopia (ageing sight), osteoarthritis of the hip and chronic gastritis, the measurement becomes much more difficult, because of the uncertainty of the threshold level above which disease, disorder or disability is considered to be present. Thus, when epidemiological study seeks answers to the general question in a representative random sample in order to estimate perceived need for health care, it requires a battery of health indices on which to scale the multiple relatively minor pathology that most of us live with.

HEALTH STATUS INDICES

In the context of queueing for health care, a health status index is very relevant as a formal scaling of need for treatment. Health status indices have been developed over the years for a variety of purposes, including helping to quantify the degree of disability or incapacity of patients, measuring effectiveness of therapeutic interventions and, by health economists in particular, for discussing the management of health service resources (Garrod and Bennett, 1971; Grogano and Woodgate, 1971; Fanshel, 1972; Berg, 1973; Williams, 1974; Gilson *et al.*, 1975; Bergner *et al.*, 1976; Kaplan *et al.*, 1976; Torrance, 1976). The literature on health status indices is now fairly extensive (Holland *et al.*, 1979; Brook, 1979; McDowell and Newell, 1987; Smith, 1988).

Many measurements of health and illness have their origins in the domain of psychiatric medicine, where physical or biochemical evidence of disease is sparse, and a large number of instruments have been developed initially to help clinicians define and diagnose such conditions as anxiety and depression. Many of the better known instruments have been subjected to rigorous studies of reproducibility, reliability and validity and a certain number of inter-scale comparisons have been reported. Rather less development and fewer comparisons between scales have been reported in the indices or instruments measuring physical disability. However, since many ask basically the same questions, about ability to wash oneself all over unaided or to walk more than a mile on the level, for example, one would expect broad comparability.

In scaling the degree of disability in certain physical conditions, rating scales may include some clinical tests, such as degree of flexion of the hip joint, for example (Larson, 1963; Harris, 1969). The majority of health status indices, however, rely wholly on patient self-completion questionnaires. Clinicians brought up in an environment of laboratory science often regard measurements derived from patient self-completion questionnaires as being much more subjective and variable than measurements derived from coulter counters or agar plates. However, it has been shown for a number of health status indices that reproducibility can be better than for many laboratory measurements.

Probably one of the more important disadvantages of the present range of health status indices in assessing need for treatment among waiting patients is the relative insensitivity at the healthy end of the spectrum. This is illustrated by Williams' use of the Rosser index in coronary artery bypass graft patients, where, for the majority, the scores for medically or surgically treated patients before treatment were typically .90 and .95 (Williams, 1985; Rosser and Watts, 1972). In terms of the whole range of the scale, it would seem that on either treatment the patients were in pretty good health and in little need of elaborate health care intervention. In attempting to overcome this insensitivity, Buxton and colleagues (1985) employed the Nottingham health profile (Hunt *et al.*, 1986) in their study of the benefits of transplantation surgery and Bombardier *et al.* (1986) employed a range of rating scales in evaluating a randomised trial in rheumatism.

The criticism of the use of patient self-rating scales being subjective rather than objective can be turned to advantage because health and illness are relative. An Olympic athlete with 'flu is clearly an ill athlete, in that his physical performance is below (his own) normal and a virus may be cultured, while his physical abilities may still be far above the population normal. Similarly, a strained achilles tendon would render the athlete 'ill', although he might score as perfectly healthy on a number of physical measures of illness. The insentivity of a number of indices might render them unhelpful for monitoring the athlete's illness, treatment and rehabilitation, but the subjectivity of the measurement would not. In that sense, health status indices, as they exist at present, may be quite useful in quantifying the perceived need for health care.

The patient (or patient and GP together or the GP acting on the patient's behalf) probably already views the hospital waiting list with some appreciation of a health status index for that condition, even if not explicitly expressed. The very lengths of the queues for some operations, like hip replacement, are evidence of the perceived low health status of patients with moderate or severe arthritis of the hip and are testimony to the success of the operation and to the expectations of quality of life improvements following the operation. Patients perceive need because of the pain and incapacity they are experiencing and because they are advised that medical technology can offer them an improvement in health status. They translate that perceived need into demand by joining the queue.

WHO IS JOINING THE QUEUE?

Routine statistics tell remarkably little about who is in the queue and nothing about who is joining it. The 'bed state' statistical return (SH3) includes for each specialty an estimated point prevalence of the inpatient waiting list. This has been tabulated nationally only once yearly, although many regions report quarterly. More recently, following the Korner report (Steering Group on Health Services Information, 1982), some districts have tabulated point prevalence monthly and/or for individual consultants within each specialty. However, it should be appreciated that what is tabulated by health authorities is only a simple and crude number of patients, without details of age, sex, personal diagnosis, seriousness of illness or degree of incapacity or duration of wait. The waiting lists are seldom regularly and routinely revised and thus the crude numbers frequently include 'ghost' patients. In addition, the statistical reports, derived from the 'bed state' return, seldom get further than health authority meetings. Industrious researchers, who know what they are looking for and where to look for it, may find the statistical reports, but the anxious potential patient is very unlikely to do so. The reports, when found, tell little other than that waiting is largely for surgery, orthopaedic surgery, ENT surgery, ophthalmology, and gynaecology.

A more refined information system came into widespread use in most health authorities of England, Wales and Scotland some 20 years ago in the form of Hospital Activities Analysis (HAA) or Scottish Hospital Inpatient Statistics (Benjamin, 1965; Heasman, 1968). These computerised systems are capable of providing waiting statistics of inpatients who have been admitted, and are capable of providing these statistics by age, sex, consultant, specialty, diagnosis, operation, duration on list, duration in hospital and outcome. Although these data have been collected routinely for all acute (and most maternity) inpatients for most of two decades, and although the computing power has been available to analyse the data, it is somewhat surprising that there is little that reaches the public eye. There are some limitations in HAA with respect to waiting: the data include only patients who have been admitted and not those who are waiting to be admitted and, in most systems, the form is completed retrospectively, so that the 'date on waiting list' is transferred on to the HAA proforma from some other record after the patient has been admitted (and discharged). Furthermore, HAA does not include outpatients at all. Thus despite its possibilities, the system to date has told us very little about waiting lists.

The Korner committee identified several of these deficiencies in the existing information systems and recommended a minimum useful data-set based on patients with more interactive access by staff (Steering Group on Health Services Information, 1982). Patient information systems (PIS) or patient administration systems (PAS) are currently being introduced and, in theory, these are capable of providing clinicians and administrators (or managers) with 'live' statistics. In practice implementation of these computer systems appears to lag somewhat behind their potential: our own recent enquiries of PAS in several health districts to identify (i) random samples of discharged patients, (ii) age, sex and area of residence matched controls, (iii) waiting lists, have revealed incompleteness of data, inflexibility of the system or those operating the system or inability of the system to do the job and so these requests of PAS have all been abandoned.

With the intention of helping the public to 'shop around' for hospitals with shorter queues, the College of Health (1987) has given publicity in recent years to the basic statistics of waiting, the crude numbers of waiting patients, the proportion of non-urgent waiting over one year and the proportion of urgent waiting over one month, derived from the 'bed state' returns. These reports have helped to bring into the open, some of the more remarkable inter-district and inter-hospital differences, but they give only simple statistics and tell nothing of who is waiting, of what patients are waiting for or which disability patients are experiencing while waiting.

In the long history of waiting for health care there have been many ad hoc studies of waiting lists, usually of individual specialties and often initiated as a response to perceived waiting list problems in a specialty. Many studies have reported little more than the point prevalence or numbers on the list (Buttery and Snaith, 1980), but some have studied who is waiting in rather more detail and have reported the basic epidemiological characteristics (age, sex, area of residence) of the list (Davidge *et al.*, 1987). Others again have investigated further and reported something of the conditions of waiting patients (provisional diagnosis, disability on some health status index) and their need for treatment or care (Bloom and Fendrick, 1987; West and Jenkins, 1984; West *et al.*, 1991).

The findings in such studies are generally unexciting and, indeed, because unexciting, are not popular with journal editors. The age and sex distributions of waiters are similar to those of admitted patients and waiters mostly report some significant, though not severe, disability or pain. Overviews of waiting or studies of all specialty waiting generally describe a similar perspective: that the bulk of the waiting problem lies in the surgical specialties and most waiters are waiting for relatively few operations for relatively few non-life threatening conditions (Grundy *et al.*, 1956; Jones and McCarthy, 1978; Davidge *et al.*, 1987).

PLANNING THE QUEUES

In health care planning, the aim is to find and develop resources to meet demands, within the framework of the overall objective of the health service. The philosophy underlying the NHS includes equal access according to need (Beveridge, 1942; HMG, 1946). While fine in theory, the practice is more problematical, because, as discussed in the previous section, 'absolute need' is somewhat enigmatic and a fair (equal) assessment of perceived need is probably unobtainable, even with detailed information on all treatments of all conditions. The geographical variation in provision of health care services in England and Wales has been the subject of discussion for most of this century and this dimension of unfairness (or of unequal opportunity) is further discussed in Chapter 6.

We might usefully consider here the arguably more important dimension of potential unfairness (or of potentially unequal opportunity) which arises from the very variable provision of health care resources between diseases. The previous section referred briefly to the 'epidemiology' of waiting lists and showed that waiting is a feature of some diseases or conditions but not of others. Application of the fairness principle would require the health service planner to balance out those queueing inequalities, if it were possible to compare need across different conditions. This may be a suitable application for the judicious use of health status indices, and, in time, their use may help the health care planner in the difficult decisions regarding distribution of health service resources between specialties and between potential patient groups (Williams, 1988).

Some health status indices have been employed to compare patients with different medical conditions (Williams, 1985; Hunt *et al.*, 1986) and others are probably suitable. Their power to achieve these comparisons is of course limited, as in any economic comparison, because the comparisons are of unlike articles, conditions or states. Who is to say whether hip pain and physical immobility in an elderly woman is more severe or less severe than heart pain and psychological incapacity in a young man and who is to say how much of one balances how much of the other? In population terms these scales may appear quite robust and may distinguish quite effectively between groups by age, by condition and by degree of disability, but they are not so good at diagnosing individuals and in general they do not work as 'clinical tests'. Again the scaling exercise is useful in so far as it makes more explicit the value judgements that are made in ranking priorities.

In theory a more rational approach to planning the health service, which in the relatively underfunded NHS implies planning for waiting, might be expected if fair and representative samples of patients waiting for hospital treatment were scaled before admission and were scaled again after hospital treatment and discharge. With suitable indices, it should be possible to identify which conditions were more or most amenable to treatment and how great the gains were. This has been done in certain selected conditions like heart transplantation, where the resource implications are significant (Buxton *et al.*, 1985). A number of the answers are very predictable, such as the huge improvement in quality of life after hip replacement, but one suspects that there might also be a number of surprises, that a number of patients are admitted for quite complicated procedures for relatively small gains in health status. One could also examine the subsequent change in health status among those patients deemed non-urgent, and obliged to wait, and those admitted early. Again there may be some surprises: many of the conditions obliged to wait are just those conditions which benefit from specialist intervention in hospital. (West *et al.*, 1991).

The rational application of scarce health care resources might take more cognisance of these potential quality of life improvements among patients with 'waiting conditions' *vis-à-vis* the relatively small benefits that are achieved in many patients with 'urgent admission conditions'. While full equity is unachieveable, because comparison of unlike costs and benefits invariably involving prejudicial value judgements is invidious, more open discussion of the relative gains would lead to more equitable resource allocation. The health planner has to employ the economic approach and trade off one disease group against another. There is a cost to society for each health-care programme, because the alternative use of resources would be for some other patient group.

This perhaps strikes at the root explanation of the chronic non-urgent waiting lists in the NHS, which have been shown to comprise relatively few conditions, and, although large in numbers, are really quite small as a proportion of total throughput (Jones and McCarthy, 1978; Frankel,

1989). It would seem that there is a tacit agreement to dump some 'no- hopers' on to a waiting list, without adequate explanation that, for them, the list leads nowhere, because the service is for them deemed ineffective, and consequently that they will be continuously passed by other patients, whose conditions are considered to be more likely to respond to treatment.

It is often said by health economists that the market in health care is unusual because the doctor controls both supply and demand. This is probably an oversimplification. While doctors certainly advise both supplier and demander, in many instances the doctors are different, as the GP advises the patient on demand while the specialist advises the health planner on supply. The specialist is the principal controller of use of health care resources and can also influence secondary demand when, after the patient has demanded and obtained an outpatient assessment, the specialist advises on the definitive and expensive treatment. Then, however, the planning has been done, the supply is largely prescribed and the argument has already moved on to management of the queue.

MANAGING THE QUEUES

Although planning is evolutionary, with relatively few exceptions, evolution and change in large organisations like the NHS are rather slow. In the short term, changes are effected within previously determined resource constraints by judicious management. While planning the queues might be considered a somewhat facetious section title, it is more widely appreciated by staff, patients and politicians that managing queues features highly in the management of the NHS. The demand side of most inpatient waiting needs little explanation; for the most part the waiting is by patients with relatively few conditions, who reasonably look forward to significant improvements in health status.

The supply side is probably more complicated. Within a given resource and provision scenario the queues can be varied quite dramatically by specialists. They may set a severe admission threshold and only add quite severely disabled patients at a rate comfortably below the average operation rate of their firm, even allowing for emergency or immediate admissions, or they may increase the firm's operation rate and/or hospital discharge rate to match a pre-determined (or preconceived) disability threshold. Alternatively they may set a less severe admission threshold and offer patients the prospect of a marginal benefit (after a long wait) and add patients to the list at a higher average rate than their operation and hospital discharge rate. In this case the queue would naturally lengthen until an equilibrium establishes, with patients declining to join because of the predicted duration of waiting, and with patients dropping out of the queue through age, emigration or seeking treatment elsewhere.

With sufficient primary referrals, specialists have the power to increase or decrease their inpatient lists quite dramatically. They may wish to do this to demonstrate demand to managers and planners in their health authority or to colleagues in competitor specialties, or to raise their prestige among referring GPs or to encourage private practice (see also Frankel and Robbins in Chapter 5). Ever since the formation of the NHS, specialists have been allowed to work both for the service and for themselves. The existence of private practice cohabiting with state-funded practice cuts against the underlying principle of the NHS. A direct competition between private practice and the NHS might be less perturbing than the murky overlap which prevails. In direct competition, patients would have a choice, balancing one service against the other. With the contracts under which many specialists work for the NHS, there is potential conflict of interest, with the ever-present possibility of earning very significant private fees from patients first identified through the NHS. Patients know about private practice and may perceive pressure to go private to obtain a faster service, even when pressure is not applied.

Clearly there are justifiable reasons why some patients with some conditions should wait longer for treatment than others. Most hospitals operate a 3 degree scale of urgency: immediate (which usually does lead to immediate or near immediate admission and hence not to inclusion in the waiting list statistics at all), urgent (for which the guideline maximum wait is one month) and non-urgent. It is not so fully appreciated that there are degrees of urgency within these bands, in particular within the non-urgent band, and we suspect that a proportion of patients are deemed so non-urgent that they are repeatedly overlooked and overtaken by others more recently added to the list.

There have been a number of calls for more systematic management of waiting lists (Fordyce and Phillips, 1970; Mason, 1976; Dalziel and Kerr, 1987) and this is now becoming a more reasonable demand of management, with the more widespread availability of computing in medical records departments. There have also been calls for more systematic ordering of waiting priority. These tend to include scales (of about 3 degrees) in a number of dimensions, such as clinical condition (particularly with regard to predicted rate of deterioration), health status (pain and disability), economic status (particularly regarding employment, dependents or dependency) and social factors (Luckman *et al.*, 1969; Leech and Luckman, 1970).

Some use has been made of the health status index approach to rationalising priorities in waiting lists (Leech and Luckman, 1970; Grogano, 1971; Phoenix, 1971). While the ends of the spectrum of disease are relatively easy to distinguish one from the other, we should consider whether scales like these help to distinguish more subtle differences in priority and need for treatment. They probably do to some degree in that they help referring GPs, acting on behalf of their patients, to describe or explain their need more fully, and in so far as they help health care planners to measure the pool of need. However, it is unlikely that health status indices, as we know them at present, provide fine enough detail to distinguish fairly between individuals.

EQUITY AND QUEUING

In any discussion of waiting for health care there should be some consideration of equity, and this is particularly relevant in discussion of waiting for treatment in the NHS.

The fundamental underlying principles of the NHS as expounded by its founding fathers, were 'equal access to all in need' and 'free at the point of delivery' (Beveridge, 1942; Bevan, 1946). The well-documented and oft-quoted inter-district variations in provision suggest considerable inequality of access (Working Group on Inequalities in Health, 1980). Inter-district variations in lengths of waiting list, discussed in Chapter 6, lend further support, but are not such reliable evidence as variation in provision, as we have seen that waiting list lengths are influenced by provision, perceived need, demand, management and even the waiting lists and waiting statistics themselves.

Equality in provision of health care for the treatment and care of different diseases and conditions is significantly more difficult to achieve, because we lack the universal scale by which different conditions may be directly compared. Nevertheless, NHS planners and managers should bear in mind the principle of equal opportunity in their decisions to provide for the treatment of certain diseases, at the expense of others. Even if the measures of comparison are imperfect, disparities should be exposed and discussed publicly, since the NHS is a public service and a public utility.

The existence of private practice means that health care in its totality is not equitable, since some have the financial means to purchase treatment in the private sector. It is often argued that private practice relieves demand on the NHS and, consequently, it might be reasoned that this reduced demand would allow for more equitable distribution of services for those remaining dependent on the public sector. However, when it comes to case mix, it could equally well be argued that it is private practice, in particular private surgery for a limited list of relatively straightforward conditions or non-life threatening conditions (in other words, the waiting list conditions), which encourages NHS planners, managers and practitioners to rank these conditions as less worthy of their attention, draws resources away from treating these conditions and hence creates case mix inequity.

SUMMARY: QUEUING AND RATIONALITY

From the point of view of the waiting patient the service looks formidable, waiting seems unreasonable, or even unnecessary, and waiting for health care could appear to be irrational.

Outpatient waiting is in many respects more irrational than inpatient waiting, in the sense that patients often know relatively little of what health improvements they may expect, what they may have to undergo in the process and how long they may have to wait for each stage. Outpatient waiting appears to be irrational also in that doctors on both the demand (GP) and supply (specialist) sides often know little of the condition of individual patients, of the statistics of the waiting list or of the condition of others on the waiting list in order to judge the relative needs of individuals on the list. Studies of selected long lists have shown that patients may (i) not know that they are waiting, (ii) have recovered or 'learned to live' with the disability, (iii) have already been treated, or (iv) report significant deterioration of their condition or health since they were added to the list (West and McKibbin, 1982; Frankel *et al.*, 1989).

The paternalistic might argue that patients do not need to know how much they will benefit or may benefit from a specialist intervention, since the decision to refer, medicate or operate is often made on their behalf. Yet whoever makes the decision, knowledge of potential benefit is essential to make the decision rationally. There is little point in adding to a list a patient with a chronic condition that is not amenable to treatment. Although the direct cash cost to the individual may not appear great, the implied indirect costs of waiting, in that the patient could be pursuing some other hope, and the emotional costs when, at the consultation after a long wait, it is explained that nothing can be done, may be considerable.

Interaction between the public health service and private practice imposes on patients seeking specialist treatment another cost in facing the decision to join the queue and wait for their 'just deserts', having already paid their premium by way of taxation, or swallow the doctor's bait and pay the private fee. Again, as in making any decision, patients need information, and to make a rational decision they need reliable information. The length of the NHS wait will undoubtedly influence the price that they will be prepared to pay to jump the queue.

From the point of view of the whole public funded and resource limited service, several of the above arguments may be used to suggest that there is a rationality in the waiting list. If demand is relatively elastic, waiting lists help to keep some of the trivia and some of the chronic incurables at bay and, if professional time is more highly valued by the service than patients' time, queuing adds to the efficiency in the use of these scarce resources.

Overall the economic balance is achieved, in so far as it is an economic balance, by the collective behaviour of individual patients, by health care planners and by the specialists, who can exert so much control over their lists. Patients are deciding whether or not to join a queue on the basis of their perceived need and their expectations of some benefit. They may be poorly informed as to their health expectations and as to queue decision strategy, particularly in the outpatient queue (Frankel *et al.*, 1989). Providers or planners are making decisions about supply, largely on the basis of unmet demand (the queue) and throughput (hospital discharge rates), which are largely for different 'non-waiting' conditions. Throughput is highly dependent on provision and therefore much of the health planner's reasoning is circular.

Waiting for health care in this country could be considerably rationalised by more patient-specific and condition-specific information for planners and managers and by more queuing information for the players or waiters.

CHAPTER 4

Opening the Gate: Referrals from Primary to Secondary Care

Stephen Farrow and David Jewell

Following on from the more theoretical concerns of the first three chapters, and in line with the idea of a progression through the various aspects of obtaining health care in this country, we have arrived at the point where patient and general practitioner interact to obtain assessment and / or treatment.

This chapter therefore examines the whole area of GP referral, from statistics of referral rates, through the reasons why GPs decide to refer at all to those factors which influence that decision and the way in which they put it into operation. With GPs firmly at the interface between society and hospital care, the various interpretations of the functions of waiting lists are considered, together with a little informed speculation about the effect of the provisions of the 1990 NHS and Community Care Act, particularly budget-holding, on GP referrals in the future.

REFERRALS IN THE UNITED KINGDOM

In 1985 there were approximately 250 million consultations in the United Kingdom, an increase of 9% since 1975. In the same year there were 62 million outpatient attendances, of which 23 million were new referrals. These figures represented increases of 11% and 12% respectively since 1975. New outpatient referrals therefore represented approximately one in three of all outpatient visits during this period and occurred following one in eleven of general practice consultations. Similarly the patients consulting their general practitioners are only a small proportion of those experiencing symptoms of illness. Clearly the relationship between the number of patients seen in general practice, the number of new referrals and the total number of outpatient attendances forms a complex system which may be difficult to control.

For the total number of outpatient attendances, the number of new referrals from general practitioners is the crucial variable. At present they refer 9% of their 250 million consultations annually. An increase in the referral rate from 9% to 10% would amount to 2.5 million more outpatient referrals, leading to an 11% increase in new referrals, or a 4% increase in all attendances. An increase of this magnitude would be extremely difficult to accommodate, with no increase in other resources, and would dwarf the waiting list 'problem'.

It is striking that such large fluctuations in numbers of referrals are not generally observed; their absence suggests that the system possesses some built-in stability. Nevertheless, it is the theoretical ability of general practitioners collectively to determine the adequacy of expensive secondary care resources that has begun to preoccupy health service managers.

ACCESS TO SECONDARY CARE

The idea of referral is implicit in a system which encourages those working within it to develop particular skills. Some referral process would exist between specialists, as it does to a small extent in the United Kingdom, if there were no generalists at all. Referral from primary to secondary care doctors is a feature of the separation of doctors into generalists, working in the community, and specialists, with access to hospital resources and beds. This process began in the early years of this century with changes in National Health Insurance to improve public access to health care. It led to a free general practitioner service for some working men whose wages fell below a specified level, although it excluded wives and children and the elderly. Patients who sought medical care would have to visit the doctor's surgery, except for the privileged few who were visited by the doctor in their own homes.

The hospital at this time was a voluntary hospital which provided both inpatient and outpatient treatment, but only for the indigent or necessitous poor (see also Chapters 1 and 5). Such hospitals were built and supported from voluntary and charitable contributions, and donations to the hospital bought privileges for the donor. In 1883, for example, 'every person who shall make a donation of 10 guineas shall be a Governor for life' (Aldis, 1984). Patients were normally seen only on the presentation of a Governor's letter which was of standard form. For general practitioners to be able to refer patients to such hospitals they would have to be in possession of such a letter, or would have to know one of the Governors sufficiently well to be able to obtain one. The only exception to this form of referral was, as it still is, to turn up at the casualty Department.

The consultant staff who worked in the voluntary hospitals were honorary, receiving no payment, but their honorary status was of critical importance as a mark of recognition and meant that they could be confident of commanding a substantial private practice. As consultants excluded general practitioners from voluntary hospitals the referral system evolved. An etiquette developed whereby consultants were called in for a second opinion.

The referring role of general practitioners is sometimes described as the gatekeeper role. This term implies that it is one of limiting patients' access to secondary care. Where resources are finite, then limiting access has positive value in ensuring that they are available when they are needed. However, it is odd to use a term which has such strongly negative connotations. In systems based on fee for item of service payments the secondary care institution might have a different perspective, wishing to encourage referral and valuing high-referring doctors. For instance, in North American teaching hospitals, a University-funded Department of Primary Care may be justified because of its ability to generate income for the hospital (Schneeweiss *et al.*, 1989). Ideally referral would have the function of ensuring easy, appropriate and efficient access to secondary care for all those able to benefit from it. It would then be a clear expression of the ethical principle of equity, and imply both limiting access in order to keep access open, and encouraging access to those likely to benefit.

Generous provision of primary care resources has been shown to diminish secondary care use (Sjønell, 1986). Comparative data from different countries show that those countries providing free and open access to primary care, and restricting access to secondary care to those referred from primary care, consistently spend less on health care than those which allow free access to secondary care (Sjønell, 1990). Such findings confirm the pivotal role for primary care doctors in the efficient running of the whole service. This suggests that those countries, like the United Kingdom, which restrict access to secondary care in this way, may have stumbled unwittingly on the most efficient model.

One more role of the referral process concerns the working of the hospital. If secondary care resources are to be used to maximum efficiency, then general practitioners need to keep them supplied with a constant flow of work. Waiting lists can also, therefore, be seen as a mechanism for ensuring the most efficient use of hospital resources and aspects of organisational change which would affect the function of waiting lists are explored further in Chapter 6.

The role of a doctor encouraging appropriate access is not always easy to combine with that of a gatekeeper. In ancient mythology the soul was ferried across the river Styx by Charon, the boatman, and the entrance was guarded by the three-headed dog Cerberus. For general practitioners these two roles have been combined. The resulting tension is one reason why the ideal model described above is difficult to detect in reality and only rarely celebrated in public debate.

THE DECISION TO REFER

The Leeuwenhorst declaration defines a general practitioner as a doctor who provides 'personal, primary and continuing care to individuals, families, and a practice population, irrespective of age, sex and illness' (Leeuwenhorst Working Party, 1974). The tasks included in this definition are already wide-ranging, so that the responsibility extends beyond the individual person in the consulting room both to this person over time, and to others in the surrounding social environment. Such responsibilities bring some immediate and practical benefits to the doctors: knowledge of the patients' past, and of their physical and social environment should make it easier to understand the nature of the problem and take more effective action.

A further role is that of patient advocacy, helping patients to understand and get the best out of the hospital system. This implies not only encouraging them to use hospitals when appropriate, but also protecting them from the potential harm of attending hospital doctors, particularly when no benefit is likely, and protecting them from unreasonable expectations of what hospital doctors will achieve. In some cases individual consultants like to control the future management of the patient, and when this happens the general practitioners may find themselves becoming little more than agents of the hospital system. Therefore, for their own professional satisfaction, general practitioners also try to avoid the secondary care system 'taking over' the primary care of the patient.

Sometimes, as with some acute surgical conditions, the decision to refer is straightforward. At other times referral to a hospital specialist may be only one of a large number of options. For instance, for a patient with a psychological problem the options include simple counselling and support, pharmacological and non-pharmacological measures prescribed by the doctor of first contact, referral to other doctors or paramedical workers within the primary health care team and various forms of complementary medicine, as well as referral to a psychiatrist. Even where the decision is a simple one of referring now, later or not at all, for conditions such as benign prostatic hypertrophy, or dysfunctional uterine bleeding, there is wide discretion for both doctor and patient when assessing the severity of symptoms, and the balance of risks and benefits of the considered procedure.

General practitioners are confronted with a number of diagnostic situations. In cases where the patient's condition or discomfort does not appear to have a significant pathological cause general practitioners seek to provide reassurance. In other cases they diagnose significant disease but prefer to treat rather than refer. In her study Dowie (1983) analysed the reasons for referral: to help in establishing diagnosis (50%); to obtain advice on treatment (25%); to reassure doctor, patient or family (10%); to respond to medical reports (10%); and to request a closed test (5%). This study confined itself to only one hospital specialty, general medicine, and therefore probably underestimated requests for hospital treatments. A later study of all referrals showed that 35% were for investigation or diagnosis, 35% for particular treatments or operations, 14% for advice on management, 9% requests for consultants to take over cases and 4% for reassurance of general practitioner or patient (Coulter *et al.*, 1989). Similar results from the studies of de Alarcon and Hodson (1964), Chamberlain (1966) and McMullan and Barr (1964) would suggest that the reasons for referral have changed very little over the last 15 years.

Referral to confirm a provisional diagnosis involves using the consultant in the way that was envisaged when the NHS was set up. A further reason for referral is concerned with the consultant as the authority who can exclude a particular diagnosis. This has implications for the continued management of problems in general practice, since it removes the threat or danger of a missed diagnosis and means that the general practitioner can continue with more certainty, even if the condition itself is chronic and difficult to manage.

The referral represents a general practitioner's and patient's joint decision to involve a third party in the management of a problem. Considerations such as those above emphasise the range of possible tasks to be addressed and the importance of clear communication between patients, general practitioners and hospital specialists. Studies of the content of referral letters and their replies have shown deficiencies in this process on the part of both sets of doctors, and suggestions that referral letters are still not thoroughly read (Jacobs and Pringle, 1990).

REFERRAL RATES

Observation of the referral process has mostly focussed on rates of general practitioners' referral to hospital specialists. The wide variation in referrals rates has been reviewed by Wilkin and Smith (1987a; 1987b). They consider fifteen studies from 1961–87 and describe variations in referral rates from 2.5 to 5.4 per 100 consultations in general practice and from 4.0 to 13.2 per 100 patients on the general practitioner list (Barber, 1971;

Birmingham Research Unit, 1978; Crombie, 1984; Cummins *et al.*, 1981; Evans and McBride, 1968; Forsyth and Logan, 1968; Fraser *et al.*, 1974; Fry, 1972; Gillam, 1985; Marsh and McNay, 1974; Morrell *et al.*, 1971; Scott and Gilmore, 1966; Starey, 1961; Williams, 1970; Wright, 1968).

In the face of such variation it is hard to see all referral decisions as objective and rational. Consideration of the complex web of factors which affect the referral decision and its implementation is instructive.

FACTORS AFFECTING REFERRAL RATES

Patient factors

The denominator for calculating referral rates depends on the composition of general practitioners' lists. These are more or less based on geographically distinct areas which confer some form of distinct bias in terms of age, sex or socio-economic category. All three biases affect patterns of morbidity: the effects of class have been explored at length in the Black report (Townsend and Davidson, 1982); older age groups are known to suffer from more chronic disease, as are women when compared with men. The effects of case mix on variations in both referral and consultation rates have been predicted (Jones, 1989). However there has been little evidence to substantiate it, since objective methods of measuring morbidity have proved notoriously difficult to devise.

As will be discussed further below, some variations in referral rates will be accounted for by the choice of denominator. If current practice of expressing rates as a proportion of consultations is followed (Roland *et al.*, 1989), they will be altered by patient factors affecting demand for general practitioner care.

The concept of illness behaviour has been the subject of considerable study during the last forty years. Illness behaviour is concerned with the interpretation of symptoms, and the way in which contact is made with the health care system. It is shaped by culture, social development and personal needs (Mechanic, 1986). Balint (1964) was one of the first to question why the patient had chosen to present at a particular time and with a particular set of symptoms. Studies in which individuals record symptoms, either by recall over a brief period, or by keeping daily symptom diaries, have demonstrated repeatedly that the majority of symptoms are handled without being reported to a doctor. This phenomenon has been termed the 'illness iceberg' (Last, 1963).

The ratio of symptoms experienced to those reported varies widely in the studies published. Overall the proportion reported is lower in those using symptom diaries than in those relying on recall, from 1 in 5

(Wadsworth *et al.*, 1971) to 1 in 40 (Banks *et al.*, 1975). Examining the patterns of referral in more detail shows that the proportion also depends on the nature of the symptom, from 1 in 9 for sore throats to 1 in 60 for headache and 1 in 74 for nerves, depression or irritability (Scambler *et al.*, 1981). The health belief model could account for some of this variation: this tries to explain patients' behaviour in terms of their beliefs about the perceived seriousness of the symptoms and their perceived vulnerability to them. For instance, Lydeard and Jones (1989) showed that the decision to consult with upper gastrointestinal symptoms was most heavily influenced by the presence of a belief that the symptoms were likely to be caused by cancer.

Following the influence of each individual's attitudes and beliefs, the decision to consult is also affected by the advice received from friends and family. Of all symptoms reported to doctors, approximately three quarters had previously been discussed with a lay person, usually a relative (Suchman, 1967; Zola, 1973). In addition to the lay network, patients may informally consult a wide range of health professionals other than doctors, such as nurses and pharmacists. The latter group also offers individuals the choice of treating themselves with non-prescribed medicines: in one survey two-thirds of all people interviewed had taken medicines in the last two weeks, with non-prescribed preparations outnumbering prescribed ones in a ratio of two to one (Dunnell and Cartwright, 1972).

From the general practitioner's perspective, one result of such influences is that patients' behaviour can be stigmatised as inappropriate. In the study by Dunnell and Cartwright (1972), a fifth of the 307 general practitioners questioned felt that over half of their surgery consultations were trivial or unnecessary. For example, it was found that inappropriately few people would treat themselves for 'heavy cold, temperature and runny nose' and thus tended to 'over-consult'. On the other hand, 'headache, more than once a week for a month' would lead to more self-medication and presumably 'under-consultation'.

In the Cardiff Health Survey (Farrow *et al.*, 1988) hypothetical patients were asked how they would react to a series of problems, and their responses were compared with those of doctors. The characteristics of the appropriate reactors, the over-reactors and under-reactors showed significant differences with regard to sex, social class and educational levels. Appropriate reactors were more likely to be female, social class I or II, single and less likely to be widowed or educated only to elementary level. The over-reactors showed no sex differences; fewer social classes I and II and more social classes IV and V; more of those educated to elementary school only; and an excess of those over 65. Amongst the under-reactors there were more males; fewer social classes I and II and more IV and V; fewer of those educated to elementary level only; fewer single people and more widowed.

Such conclusions depend on doctors' judgment of appropriateness. Hannay (1980) tried to quantify patients' own judgement by getting them to grade their own symptoms for pain, disability and seriousness. Of those with symptoms causing severe pain or disability, 26% did not seek professional medical advice, while 11% of those with symptoms causing no pain or disability referred themselves to the general practitioner. Both of the groups could be described as behaving inappropriately, and this conclusion is based only on their own definitions.

Patients' explicitly stated requests for referral (patient demand) are a variable component in reasons for referral. Patients will differ in the extent to which they perceive symptoms to be serious and the benefits they expect to get from a specialist referral. They will also differ in their ability and willingness to express their own wishes to a general practitioner. 'Patient demand' may represent a small part of the total reasons for referrals, but this in itself shows that there is scope for a substantial increase. There is little information concerning this aspect of referral, possibly because it is not seen by professionals as an acceptable reason. In any case, patients' demands may operate at an unstated level, encouraging general practitioners to refer for a diagnostic opinion in cases where they themselves are reasonably certain of the diagnosis. There is a widely held view that patients value general practitioners who refer more, although it may not rank very highly as one of a list of important attributes (Smith and Armstrong, 1989).

Understanding patients' behaviour has long been seen as a vital component of good general practice. It might be thought that such understanding would enable doctors to separate the clinical condition from the way in which it is expressed by the patient, and thus improve the effectiveness of their decision making, including referral to secondary care. Even if such perfect understanding were attainable, the advantage would depend on a narrow definition of the value of referrals. As long as the purpose of the health service is to answer patients' individual needs, however defined, patients' behaviour will continue to exert an effect on the numbers of referrals to secondary care.

General practitioner factors

Most of the studies examining differences in rates of referrals have been conducted by general practitioners, and have tried to explain the variation by exploring general practitioner variables.

Fry (1978) reduced his referral rate from 105 to 47 per 1000 over 25 years and attributed this to greater experience, improved knowledge of the natural history of disease and greater awareness of the limitations of consultants. Others have found no association between doctors' age and referral rate (Scott and Gilmore, 1966), and one study found the opposite relationship, of referrals for obesity increasing with the age of the referring doctor (Rothert *et al.*, 1984). Increased experience might be expected to result in a lower referral rate, but the opposite relationship has also been described (Evans and McBride, 1968). This may be an effect of case mix within practices, with doctors who express a special interest in a particular topic attracting to themselves more patients with that problem. Overall, no consistent relationship has been found between doctors' age, experience and referral rates (Wright, 1968; Forsyth and Logan, 1968).

With no obvious objective factors emerging from such studies to explain the variation in referral rates, there has been a search for personal factors. Cummins *et al.* (1981) postulated unique thresholds of referral for individual doctors, without specifying of what the concept was likely to consist. Various attempts have been made to explore the components of general practitioners' personal style. Janis and Mason (1977) developed a conflict model of decision-making in accordance with Lewin's analysis (1958). They saw man as a reluctant decision-maker, 'beset by conflict, doubts and worry, struggling with incongruous longings, antipathies and loyalties and seeking relief by procrastinating, rationalising or denying responsibilities for his own choices'. Questions that might be asked by general practitioners would typically take the form: 'are the risks to the patient serious if I don't refer now?'; 'are the risks to me (my esteem) serious if I refer now?'; 'is it realistic to hope to find a better solution?' If no defensive avoidance was possible, either defensive procrastination or defensive referral would result. Finally the general practitioner might consider whether there was sufficient time to search for further information before making a decision. The difference between high and low referrals may thus largely depend on the self-confidence of the general practitioner.

However, complex research into medical problem-solving has not found an association between personality variables and clinical problem-solving measures. Instead, general practitioners' sense of professionalism would appear to produce a balanced tension in their relationship with consultants and they appear concerned with both the maintenance of standards in referral letters and with the prevention of abuse or misuse of consultants caused by inappropriate referrals.

A substantial part of the explanation for the variability in referrals may lie in the cognitive process of general practitioners, with different levels of confidence in their own clinical judgement, different levels of awareness of the base rate probabilities of the occurrence of life-threatening events, different current states of medical knowledge, and different levels of reliance on certain technical investigations, notably ECGs and biochemistry. They may also differ in their levels of keenness to sustain the esteem of consultants.

Grol *et al.* (1985) have used questionnaires to identify attitudes held by general practitioners, and to group them by the patterns revealed. Attention has particularly focussed on general practitioners' tolerance of risk, with the suggestion that those doctors least willing to take risks would have high referral rates. Differences between doctors in different European countries have been identified which suggest marked differences between different medical cultures (Grol *et al.*, 1990). By concentrating on only one aspect of risk, this model excludes other aspects discussed above, such as the doctors' view of the risk to patients' health both of referring and not referring, as well as the risks to their professional reputation, in their own eyes and those of their specialist colleagues, of inappropriate referral. Such analysis may prove to be most useful for postgraduate education, helping trainees to appreciate the importance of understanding their own attitudes, and how they might be modified.

Factors of practice organisation

Type of practice could influence referral rates in either direction. Large list sizes would give doctors less time to spend with their patients, but this could make them more likely to refer as a way of dealing with demands, or less likely, if less time means that they are less likely to identify a problem that could benefit from secondary referral. Similar arguments apply to factors which increase doctors' chances of knowing their patients well, such as operating a personal list within a group practice.

Starey (1961) reported higher rates of referral for doctors with large lists and those in urban areas, but this has not been confirmed in other studies (Wright, 1968; Scott and Gilmore, 1966). Sorensen (1986) found that general practitioners in single-handed practices had higher rates of referral than those in partnership. A recent study in Holland by Wijkel (1986) suggests that referrals are lower from health centres where there is a primary care team. However, as with other factors, no consistent pattern has been found in the United Kingdom.

General practitioners may be able to influence the denominator for referral rates by encouraging or discouraging patients to consult. Consultation rates also show wide variation. The study of consultation in general practice carried out by Williams (1970) described 60 000 consultations with 67 general practitioners and commented on the wide variation. The average number of consultations per general practitioner per week was 229, with a range of 59 to 502. The mean rate of consultation per 1000 patients per year was 5456, which compared with 3938 from the National Morbidity Survey (Royal College of General Practitioners, 1979).

Registration with a general practitioner may be determined by historical family ties or by considerations of distance when moving to a new address. Distance from home to practice is clearly an important consideration and many general practitioners operate a cut-off system based on distance. However, this may be more related to the problems for general practitioners responding to requests for home visits than to those for the patients in attending the surgery. In the Williams (1970) survey the mean consultation rates for rural practices were lower than for urban practices. They also tended to be lower for doctors who had been in practice for more than ten years. Other barriers to access may be the attitudes of staff, including the doctor, practice nurse and receptionist. Some patients see appointment systems as a further barrier; others see the absence of an appointment system as the barrier.

Consultation with the general practitioner may include telephoning the general practitioner for advice. In the Cardiff Health Survey (Farrow *et al.*, 1988) the public was confronted with a series of hypothetical situations. 'Telephoning the general practitioner for advice' was selected by an average of 15% of respondents for all situations. Hallam (1991) has shown a wide variation in general practitioners' willingness to consult with patients by telephone.

Within a practice of several general practitioners individual doctors' patterns of work will reflect their personal interests and experience, the expectations that patients have of them and sometimes particular formal arrangements within the practice. This is most clearly seen in the work patterns of trainees, who see more acute problems than established principals, and of women doctors, who see more female-related problems (Preston-Whyte *et al.*, 1983; Cooke and Ronalds, 1985). Such deviations from the average work pattern will lead to predictable variations in referral patterns. For instance, a doctor who sees a disproportionate number of a practice's elderly population would be expected to have a high rate of referral.

General practitioners can also reduce referrals by increasing the amount of work they are prepared to undertake in their own practices. The provisions to pay general practitioners for minor surgery have been created with this purpose in mind, although it is not certain that it will have the desired effect. As with any fee for item of service system, it may merely encourage general practitioners to treat some conditions, such as excision of cysts or lipomata, that they would previously have left untreated, or others, such as intra-articular injections for arthritis, that they would previously have treated with drugs. If any action is to have a referral-sparing effect it may need to be quite specific. For instance, the small number of general practitioners who still take responsibility for intrapartum care refer fewer pregnant women to specialists. Where practices organise a structured programme for patients with particular chronic conditions there will be reduced demand for outpatient clinic services. The reduction will, however, be in repeat, rather than new attendances, and will not necessarily be reflected in any change in referral rates.

Hospital factors

The availability of a particular service is a self-evident prerequisite for a general practitioner to refer to it: referrals to cardiac surgeons for coronary artery bypass surgery do not occur when the only available treatment for angina is medical. When a new hospital was opened in Milton Keynes the referral rates from the nearby practices increased slightly, although variation in rates between the practices was much greater than between the two time periods before and after opening the new hospital (Noone *et al.*, 1989).

Availability may be altered in more subtle ways than by the presence or absence of particular services. For instance, when waiting lists for procedures such as varicose vein surgery become very long surgeons may 'close' the list and not accept further referrals. Conversely, general practitioners notice when waiting lists are shorter and refer other cases that they would previously have managed in other ways. Specialists may signal their 'availability' in the way they react to patients and therefore encourage or discourage referrals for certain problems. They can also vary availability by the extent to which they and their junior staff give patients appointments for follow-up attendances at outpatient clinics.

There is considerable variation in the arrangements for general practitioners to have open access to certain diagnostic or treatment services. In particular, requests for some radiological tests or physiotherapy in some districts may only be made following referral to a specialist, and in others can be made direct by the general practitioners. Wright (1968) and Forsyth and Logan (1968) found no correlation between doctors' use of open access facilities and their referral rates to outpatients, whereas Backett *et al.* (1966) found these to be positively correlated. Dowie's work (1983) on open access radiology suggests that the average number of requests per month was 13 per general practitioner. There was no correlation between the amount of X-ray use and the rate of outpatient referral. Requests for pathology tests were commoner among the younger general practitioners, while referral to outpatients was found to be influenced by the waiting time for open access diagnostic tests. Predictably, the introduction of a new programme for breast screening has been found to increase referral rates (Ashby *et al.*, 1990).

Summary

To describe the patterns of referral decisions, Dowie (1983) developed a framework comprising three groups of elements. The first of these included professional attributes: medical (clinical) knowledge, clinical judgement, and medical practice. The second group of factors included knowledge of the health care system and, particularly, general practitioners' judgement of specialists and specialties. General practitioners were likely to take account of the style of particular consultants as well as their special expertise when deciding where to send their patients. They also tended to keep to particular consultants for the referral of particular problems. Dowie asked how general practitioners form an opinion of consultants' competence. It was found that opinions based on their training were often wrong, but that general practitioners might be influenced by the consultants' ability in handling patients and their use of informal discussions. Organisational factors were equally important and included distance, access, availability of transport, the scheduling of outpatients' sessions and waiting times. The third group of factors in the referral decision related to the general practitioners' personal style and their judgement of patients' values.

Wilkin and Smith (1987a) have produced a more general model of referral. Nevertheless, their alternative model uses the same basic ingredients and again emphasises the culture of general practitioner/consultant and general practitioner/hospital relationships and stresses the central importance of the general practitioner's personal style and sense of professionalism.

Factors associated with methods of measurement

Referral rates are subject to the vagaries of the measuring instrument used. Various denominators have been suggested. Rates as a proportion of the practice population give accurate figures in terms of the overall demand for secondary services, but make no allowance for the different work patterns of individual general practitioners within a practice. In order to compare the referring behaviour of different general practitioners, the rates should ideally be broken down into different specialties and the contact rates for patients within those specialties used as the denominator. However, recording contact rates broken down by specialty is in itself an expensive exercise and, if done routinely, would be subject to wide variation in quality.

For the purpose of reporting to Family Health Service Authorities and comparisons with other doctors, therefore, the Department of Health requires general practitioner to report referrals as numbers per hundred consultations. The variation in consultation rates has already been described and, like that in referral rates, the variation defies simple explanation. Much of it appears to be demand-led. However, general practitioners may be able to vary the rate by altering the number of follow-up visits recommended, or by altering the total numbers of appointments offered. (Hospital specialists are similarly able to control their availability for new referrals.) It is not clear whether general practitioners consciously manipulate their consultation rates, but the opportunity exists if referral rates were to become a major component in determining remuneration.

Using a computer model in which referrals are randomly ditributed among consultations, Moore and Roland (1989) have shown that referral rates may be subject to considerable random variation. Many studies have reported rates based on limited periods of observation which accentuate such variation. Roland's model assumes constant underlying demand; the effect is likely to be magnified by real variations in the underlying demand for care.

Interpretation of referral rates

Given these components to the theoretical model, referral rates of general practitioners would be expected to follow a Gaussian distribution curve. The number of variables generate so much 'noise' in the system that simple associations between single variables and the overall rate would be difficult to detect. The observed figures would indeed seem to support this conclusion. By extension, experiments which attempt to modify referral rates by simple interventions are likely to be frustrated by other variables working both on the referral process itself and on the system of measurement. Such experiments would, of course, include attempts on the part of individual general practitioners to modify their behaviour in response to feedback about excessively high or low referral rates.

Confirmation for this view comes from a study from Coulter *et al.* (1989), in which general practitioners' referral rates were compared with the subsequent rates of admission to hospital. The hypothesis was that specialists should make sounder decisions, that admission rates would therefore vary less than referral rates, and that high-referring practices would have low admission rates. They found that admission rates were as variable as referring rates, suggesting just as much uncertainty exists in hospital as in general practice.

Referral rates have been analysed because recording them is the simplest and quickest way of illuminating a dark but important corner of the NHS. They are also important for those who plan and fund secondary services. However, the attempt to use rates as a proxy measure for quality seems doomed to failure. Are high-referring doctors those who refer too many patients to hospital, or those who understand, better than their peers, how much hospital services have to offer and how much patients want to use specialist expertise? Are low referring doctors the parsimonious, able ones, who do most for patients within their own surgeries and know the limitations of hospital specialists, or those who do not recognise often enough when specialists can help?

One possible way of viewing referring doctors is as screening instruments, whose job is to identify to a high degree of specificity and sensitivity those patients able to benefit from hospital services. The amount of acceptable inaccuracy then follows familiar arguments derived from screening programmes: it will usually be preferable to have false positives (people referred unnecessarily) than false negatives (people wrongly not referred). Crucially, this argument is based on the principle that there is a balance of false positives and false negatives; fewer of one will always be balanced by more of the other. If the overall system is a biological one, involving multiple factors subject to random variation, then referral rates will always follow a Gaussian distribution. The spread may appear to be too wide, but attention to the tails of those with highest and lowest rates will have little effect on the aggregate demand for secondary services. A more effective way of changing aggregate demand would be to move the whole distribution, including the mean value, by small amounts.

If the objective is to apply ethical principles of beneficence and equity in order to make the best use of the resources available, then we must abandon the idea that crude referral rates tell us anything at all about quality, and try to measure quality more directly. As yet, simple and valid methods for measuring quality are not available, although some studies have shown possible lines of attack.

For instance, Grace and Armstrong (1986) asked general practitioners, specialists and patients to classify independently the reason for referral into diagnosis, treatment, reassurance, investigation and other. There was universal agreement between all three parties in only 33% of cases. The authors suggested one possible reason for such a large discrepancy was a difference in general practitioners' and specialists' perceptions of the hospital doctor's role. In a limited study from their own practice, Emmanuel and Walter (1989) were able not only to make judgements about the appopriateness of their referrals, but also to implement a programme of agreed protocols to improve the effectiveness of later referrals.

THE FUNCTION OF WAITING LISTS

Waiting lists have for many years been seen as the only rationing device we have in a system where health care is free at the point of delivery. How this works in practice is clear given the apparent stability of the system, but substantial and visible waiting lists may deter patients from seeking hospital care, and encourage general practitioners to use both their own resources to the full and to explore all other non-hospital alternatives.

Metcalfe (1990) has described a model for the NHS in which general practitioners manage the boundary between the ever-changing needs and demands of society, and the stable, relatively inflexible institution of secondary care. Good primary care is able to maintain a responsive interface with society and a stiffer, techno-medical interface with hospital based specialist care. Waiting lists have always been seen as a feature of hospital care. While this makes sense in organisational terms, it may make better sense conceptually to see them as one of the tools which general practitioners use to manage the boundary between society and hospital care.

At least one other interpretation is possible. Waiting lists can be seen as a symbol of the NHS's values, that waiting in an orderly queue is a fundamental expression of equal access to limited resources.

REFERRALS IN THE REFORMED NHS

Until now waiting lists also had the invaluable function of allowing doctors and patients to collude in blaming their problems on the government, but the last government has focused much attention on referral in the changes that were introduced on 1st April 1991. In doing so it has created the impression that referral is the most important part, rather than just one aspect, of general practice. Devoting so much attention to referral will divert attention from clinical work within practices which, in terms of the effect on patients' health and doctors' ability to bring about change, is more likely to repay time and energy spent on quality assurance.

Surveys of general practitioner attitudes to hospital care reveal that their perceptions of both quality and adequacy are not shared by consultants and managers (Hicks and Baker, 1991). Groups of general practitioners are beginning to define what is required from the hospital and to develop practical guidelines for outpatient care. These guidelines address such questions as waiting time and whether new outpatients referrals should actually be seen by the hospital consultant rather than a junior member of the medical staff. The contractual environment is already leading to a new relationship between purchasing health authorities and general practitioners. This, together with the development of guidelines, should lead to certain improvements in hospital practice.

The effect on referrals is, however, uncertain. The changes have been presented as encouraging the service to be more responsive to consumers' wishes, and so could immediately increase demand for referrals. However, the proposals contain two mechanisms, contract and price, which may limit choice. Referrals will only be possible where a prior contract exists, and the number of referrals within a contract may be fixed.

The provisions for practices to hold their own budgets have apparently been devised to encourage general practitioners to negotiate more widely in order, among other objectives, to avoid patients having to wait. Faced with patients requesting care immediately, fund-holding doctors will find it difficult to blame the government for waiting lists. In a sense the effect is to put those practices into the position previously held by the government itself, of handling infinite demand within a limited budget.

As has been suggested above, an excess of demand can be handled in many ways without referral, or by delaying referral to the next budgetary period. It is likely that waiting lists will be managed, in one way or another, by general practitioners and will vanish from political view. The assumption is that those general practitioners who manage their own budgets will be more assiduous in guarding their patients' interests. In the long run, general practitioners willing to take on a rationing role, by holding their own budgets, may find it difficult to continue as patients' advocates. If such a shift becomes apparent to patients, then there may be profound consequences for the fundamental relationship of trust between them and their general practitioners, and that in turn could considerably increase the demand for specialist referral.

CHAPTER 5

Entering the Lobby: Access to Outpatient Assessment

Stephen Frankel and Margaret Robbins

Outpatient activity offers one of the most graphic examples of the extent to which the balance of NHS activity may elude any simple criteria of rationality. Large numbers of people are seen in outpatient clinics each year. During the financial year 1989–90, 36 262 539 outpatient attendances were recorded in England, equivalent to some 75% of the population (Government Statistical Service 1991a). Some 15% of the overall hospital budget is absorbed by outpatient activity. However, the evidence suggests that whatever rationality informs what comprises one of the major components of health care provision in Britain, the distinctive advantage in terms of care or cure to those selected for attendance may not be apparent. While large numbers of people are occupied in attendances that may be burdensome to both patient and doctor, other patients seeking urgent assessment may languish on waiting lists. The evidence for this assertion is the subject of this chapter. The changing perceptions of the nature of the problems surrounding outpatient assessment over the last century offer a graphic illustration of the ways in which professional concerns can take precedence over public preferences in debates of health policy.

The issue of outpatient referral should be straightforward. The ostensible purpose is to seek a specialist, second opinion, 'to confirm a diagnosis, to establish a course of action or provide the patient with expertise available only in hospital, such as surgery or radiotherapy' (Strang and Cone-Smith, 1989). However, if it is really the uncomplicated end of hospital activity, then why, from all accounts (including that of West in Chapter 3), is the system so resistant to rationalisation?

From the point of view of the person seeking specialist advice, the referral process (reviewed by Farrow and Jewell in Chapter 4), takes the form of an initiation into a state of 'patienthood', which can herald the beginning of repeated hospital journeys, long waiting times in clinics, and conflicting advice from various members of staff. In this chapter we enlarge on the historical perspectives introduced in Chapters 1 and 4 and examine in some detail the various suggestions which have been put forward for rationalising outpatient services, including the questions of routine follow-up after uncomplicated inpatient admission and reorganised administration of outpatient clinics. We direct attention to the impact on the men and women who are themselves outpatients, or potential outpatients, and outline the more broadly researched area of the expectations and attitudes of general practitioners and hospital doctors in handling referrals and waiting lists.

QUESTIONS RAISED BY AVAILABLE DATA

What is the evidence that outpatient services are failing to deliver appropriate care? One global indication that the wrong people may be occupying outpatient departments comes from routine data. Unfortunately data on the length of waiting times for outpatient appointments are not recorded uniformly across the United Kingdom. Unlike inpatient waiting lists, statistics for outpatient waiting lists are not collated centrally in England. However, figures are published for Wales and they can be used to indicate the extent of outpatient waiting there.

At the end of March 1988, 82 319 patients were waiting for outpatient appointments in Wales. These appointments were from the same specialties represented in the inpatient waiting lists; those on the outpatient waiting lists constitute the advance guard of the same army that later amasses on the inpatient waiting lists (see Chapter 1)

Before getting too despondent about the size of these waiting lists, it is important to set these numbers against the throughput of outpatient clinics. The figure of 82 319 patients waiting seems less daunting when it is compared with the figure of 2 272 004 outpatient attendances during the previous year in Wales. The waiting list thus represents less than 4% of the outpatient throughput.

Taking a closer look at the constitution of the waiting lists and outpatient throughput it is possible to see the beginnings of the dilemma. Of the 2 272 004 attendances in 1987, 77% were repeat attendances, which is the same as the percentage of repeat outpatient attendances in England during 1989/90 (Government Statistical Office, 1991a). In March 1988, 30 286 of the 82 319 new patients had been waiting for over 3 months. The question of outpatient waiting lists could therefore be presented in the form: why had a proportion of the patients accounting for the 1 755 244 repeat attendances not been discharged in order to accommodate the

82 000 patients who had been waiting, or at least the 30 286 who had been waiting over three months?

Stating the situation in this manner raises a number of issues which need to be addressed for the sake of the many patients who have to wait over three months for specialist advice. It has to be asked whether all the patients who are told to re-attend actually benefit from the repeat consultations, and whether limited resources are being allocated in an appropriate and efficient way. The question is not really whether consultants could see more patients, or whether more consultants could relieve the workload, but whether the existing consultants might see a different set of patients, thereby imparting greater benefit.

OUTPATIENT SERVICES IN HISTORICAL PERSPECTIVE

Controversy over the proper role of outpatient departments is not new. However what is striking about this controversy is the way that the source of complaints has shifted from one professional group to another as the organisation of British health care, and forms of remuneration, have altered.

'Abuse' is a term which has a long history in relation to outpatient services. Indeed this issue has at various times exercised some groups of medical practitioners more than any other, and at various times has taken up a considerable proportion of the column space in medical journals. The 'abuse' which engrossed so many correspondents prior to the establishment of the NHS was the mirror image of the current NHS outpatient problem. In those days the controversy concerned the ease of access to outpatient assessment. Today, the problem is perceived as the difficulty in gaining access.

There were some 1½ million recorded outpatient visits in London in 1887, for a population of 4 million (Hansard, 1889). Some relief for the impoverished was regarded as a proper role for the voluntary hospitals. However, at a time when other forms of charitable relief were restricted to the indigent through the principle of lesser eligibility, it was held that outpatient services were being used by those who could be expected to pay for medical advice. The problem was that . . . 'Gentlemen's servants, clerks and well-to-do tradespeople with their wives and children absolutely encumber the waiting rooms of the London hospitals' (Anonymous, 1853a).

The British Medical Journal of the 1850s thus reveals numerous diatribes against 'the abuse of Hospitals and Dispensaries – a monster evil of the Day', as the outpatient department 'diminishes the earnings of Physicians, surgeons and general practitioners practising within the sphere of operations of a hospital' (Anonymous, 1853a; 1853b; 1853c; 1853d).

The nub of the issue was competition between hospital consultants and general practitioners for patients. From the general practitioner's point of view, the result of outpatient practice was that: 'Those people who can best afford to pay their medical attendant liberally are usually the first to avail themselves of the means of defrauding the medical profession by obtaining their treatment at a nominal sum' (Anonymous 1875). One response of the general practitioners was to form an association called the Hospital Outpatient Reform Association (Abel-Smith, 1964:108) in order to ensure that outpatient departments were 'not abused' by persons who were able to pay. This tension also meant that general practitioners became reluctant to refer patients to consultants, lest they never got them back (Anonymous, 1878).

The current distinction between general practitioners and consultants is blurred by the parallel care conducted through outpatient departments. Since the introduction of the NHS, charges of 'abuse' lead to only intermittent and modest protest. In the later nineteenth century the division of care between hospital consultants and general practitioners was the subject of the most heated debate. The letter columns of the *British Medical Journal* became so overloaded with complaints from general practitioners, who suspected that consultants were taking their patients from them (Anonymous, 1884), that the journal closed this correspondence on the grounds that it had become too acrimonious (Anonymous, 1886). However, little was done as the 'hordes of outpatients were good for appeal purposes and were wanted by the medical staff both for teaching and for the selection of interesting inpatients' (Abel-Smith, 1964:118).

Two sets of solutions were proposed: restriction by referral or restriction by income. However, the issue grumbled on with no resolution. The whole question of eligibility for poor relief was in such disarray by the beginning of the twentieth century that a Royal Commission was appointed in 1905. The question of outpatient use was discussed in terms which are still appropriate today (Royal Commission, 1905:285).

> Suggestions for remedying the abuses of the outpatient departments have been laid before us by many witnesses, but by none more fully than the representatives of the British Medical Association. We are convinced with them that a strenuous effort should be made to circumscribe the work of the outpatient departments. They should be used exclusively for: (1) Casualties; (2) Consultations; (3) Cases requiring expensive equipment for the treatment of special diseases and defects.

The first real change in access to outpatient departments came when the National Insurance Act (1911) came into force in January 1913. Many hospitals then refused to treat insured patients, other than emergencies, unless they had been referred by their panel doctors. This change was welcomed by the British Medical Association (BMA), as it helped to 'elevate the outpatient department from its present position as a mere dumping ground . . . to its proper place in the organized service of the nation' (Anonymous, 1913). Where this referral system was instituted, the numbers of outpatients fell markedly. For example, at St. Bartholomew's, the figure fell from 120 834 in 1912 to 78 783 in 1913 (Abel-Smith, 1964:246).

The National Insurance Act (1911) reversed the previous incentives for general practitioners, as capitation encouraged referral to hospital for treatment. Now that the general practitioner had an assured income, there was no opposition to increasing work being undertaken by hospital colleagues (Abel-Smith, 1964:247).

However the 'problem of the outpatient' (British Medical Association, 1931) returned over the following decade. By 1920 outpatient attendances again exceeded the pre-1911 levels (Abel-Smith, 1964:333) and the BMA report asserted that outpatient departments should be used only for consultation. Thus the conflict returned some 20 years after the solution of the 1911 Act between general practitioners and the voluntary hospitals (particularly their outpatient departments). Correspondence in the 1930s revealed that general practitioners' grievances were unchanged from eighty years before in that 'These free clinics are usurping the place of the general practitioner . . . This is the beginning of a deliberate attack upon private practice, with the object of depleting it' (Bradlaw, 1938).

Despite BMA opposition, outpatient expansion continued from 1.5 million attendances in 1935 to 2 million in 1937 (Ministry of Health, 1938:77). This included continued treatment for discharged patients, with a priority of the hospital still being the need for 'abundant and comprehensive clinical material' (Anonymous, 1931). The controversy lingered on with different scenarios being suggested. 'Instead of general practitioners complaining about 'abuse' if hospital doctors took their cases from them, in future it would be hospital doctors who would be complaining of 'abuse' if general practitioners sent them work they did not want . . . . Instead of the nineteenth-century battle to get patients, the second half of the twentieth century might see doctors scrambling to foist patients on to their colleagues' (Anonymous, 1946).

Since the inception of the NHS, the concern over outpatient abuse has switched somewhat to criticism of consultants retaining patients unnecessarily, although this criticism is muted in comparison to the level of previous concern. An editorial in *The Lancet* (Anonymous, 1976a:1168) stated that if a consultant, takes over from the general practitioner the care of the patient . . . he ceases to be a consultant . . . Much of this work is quite unnecessary. Some of it may indeed be harmful, causing inconvenience, irritation, anxiety, and loss of earnings to the patients, and unjustified work and expense to ambulance and hospital services. Outpatient clinics could be drastically reduced – if the consultants wanted to reduce them.

An editorial in the *Journal of the Royal College of General Practitioners* (Anonymous, 1976b:762–3) concurred with *The Lancet*'s analysis, and concluded that

'Unless there are good reasons to the contrary, the follow-up of patients who have been to hospital – either as inpatients or outpatients – should be the province of the general practitioner and his team. What other simple measure could reduce the work-load of the hospital service so much and also improve the relationship between general practitioner and consultant?'

By the 1970s, there was thus a general feeling that too much strain was being placed on outpatient departments. The problem was couched in terms of wastage of resources, unnecessary demands being put on outpatients to keep returning for unrewarding follow-up, and the contention that hospital doctors were trespassing on the responsibilities that general practitioners should properly have towards patients. In the sense that patients really 'belong' to their general practitioners, they were being 'loaned' for too long to the hospital doctors.

It was in fact Loudon's article (1976) in *The Lancet* which rekindled the debate over outpatient services. The 1976 *Lancet* and *Journal of the Royal College of General Practitioners* editorials followed on, together with a string of supporting articles for Loudon's critical appraisal of routine follow-up after uncomplicated surgery (Kirk, 1976; Hopkins, 1976; Coggan and Goldacre, 1976). It is interesting that Forsyth and Logan's earlier study of hospital outpatients in the 1960s failed to spark the lively debate which Loudon's article ignited in the 1970s, although they pointed out the problem of routine follow-up patients who blocked the attendances of new referrals, and coined the terms 'season ticket-holders' and 'detainees' to describe such routine outpatient attenders (Forsyth and Logan, 1968:59)

The issue of outpatient re-attendance was thus seized on as the major contributory factor to outpatient waiting lists and the overburdening of outpatient services. However, research has been piecemeal and numerous worthy recommendations that are reviewed below have generally been ignored.

A significant characteristic of the debate on the oversubscription of out-patient services, and what to do about it, has been that attention has been focussed on the solutions to the problem rather than its causes. The main protagonists – the hospital doctors and the general practitioners – tend to agree that the system is not working well from the point of view of the waiting outpatient, and although general practitioners seem to have been willing to take their patients back from specialist treatment, little transfer appears to have occurred. Concomitantly, there seems to be little motivation to understand why a status quo may serve other interests which are more difficult to comprehend and/or condone.

In the discussion which follows, the various recommendations which have been proffered over the past fifteen years or so for rationalising outpatient services are considered, with some suggestions as to why the system has remained so impervious to change.

STRATAGEMS AND SOLUTIONS

Patients are referred to outpatient departments for a variety of reasons, as suggested by Farrow and Jewell in Chapter 4, and from a variety of sources. New referrals may originate from general practitioners or from other hospital departments, and any outpatient clinic is likely to be additionally composed of patients given follow-up appointments after an inpatient admission. Figures from 1989–90, show that 8 507 724 of the 36 262 539 outpatient attendances in England for the year were new attendances, a ratio of 1 new attendance to every 3.3 re-attendances (Government Statistical Office, 1991a).

The problem of outpatient waiting lists has been attributed to an unwillingness to discharge patients from clinics, unnecessary follow-up appointments given to patients after uncomplicated admissions instead of returning them to the care of general practitioners, and an excess of referring zeal on the part of a large proportion of general practitioners. Many solutions to this complex state of affairs have been suggested, ranging from instituting referral guidelines for general practitioners and follow-up guidelines for hospital staff, to improving appointment systems and the management of clinics, and recommending better communication between consultants and general practitioners. The retention of patients with interesting conditions for the purposes of research has been condemned as a 'pernicious habit' (Anonymous, 1976a).

Outpatient follow-up after inpatient admissions

Loudon (1976) suggested that routine follow-up after uncomplicated surgery was a considerable waste of time, effort and money. He believed that part of the reason why the system continued was the unspoken belief that working harder on behalf of patients consisted in seeing the largest possible number in a working day. Furthermore, nurses were trained to ensure that patients did not leave hospital without their follow-up appointments. He suggested that general practitioners should cancel unnecessary follow-up appointments, for which the majority of patients would be grateful (Loudon, 1976).

The debate was now opened concerning the appropriateness of outpatient services, and many of the contributions which followed considered possibilities for reform. Hopkins (1976) supported the results of Loudon's analysis that the presence of re-attenders in outpatient clinics was largely responsible for the overcrowding, and he pointed out that the possible solution of increasing the number of consultants would not necessarily result in a more effective service to patients. The number of new outpatients seen per consultant had actually declined during the previous ten years in almost every specialty.

The component of outpatient attendance which appeared to be most amenable to reform was the routine follow-up of patients after uncomplicated surgery. Coggan and Goldacre (1976) considered the value of outpatient follow-up after appendicectomy and concluded that, at most, only those patients with peritonitis at the time of operation, or those with post-operative complications merited routine follow-up. They pointed out that when complications arose which were serious enough to warrant re-admission, these were not identified by an outpatient attendance, but by the general practitioner, and that most of the complications seen at outpatients could in fact have been managed by the general practitioner.

Cochrane *et al.* (1980) and McCormack *et al.* (1984) have also evaluated the role of general practitioners in the follow-up of patients after uncomplicated surgery. The former pointed to the benefits of educating patients in the symptoms of early recurrence of carcinoma of the large bowel to save them from unnecessary and often worrying routine follow-up, with the implication that patients would take any initial problems to the general practitioner, who could then evaluate the need for re-referral. McCormack *et al.* (1984) explored the attitudes of consultants, patients and general practitioners towards follow-up after uncomplicated surgery and found that general practitioners generally felt capable of providing it in the majority of cases and were supported in this contention by the hospital doctors. Bulpitt, Daymond and Dollery (1982) compared the value of outpatient follow-up with community care for hypertensive patients and found that, for well-controlled patients, discharge back to the general practitioner was to be recommended.

Obviously not all chronic conditions nor the follow-up of acute conditions can be managed completely by the general practitioner when

particular investigations are needed. Farrelly *et al.* (1986) found differences in the treatment and follow-up of patients with gastric ulcers
when referred directly by their general practitioners for barium meals,
when compared with those referred by a consultant. The recommended
clinical management of a regime of barium meals or endoscopy until the
ulcer has healed was not adhered to as rigourously in the patients referred
by general practitioners as in the patients referred by consultants. The
authors also introduced the issue of 'open access' to investigative services
for general practitioners as a further means for reducing outpatient
attendances.

The outpatient clinic

There are various ways in which better management and administration
of outpatient clinics could improve efficiency and reduce the waiting
lists. One particularly vicious cycle is concerned with long waiting time
and non-attendance. McGlade *et al.* (1988) considered this problem and
found that prolonged waiting times from referral to appointment were
significantly related to non-attendance. West and McKibbin's (1982) study
of orthopaedic waiting lists found that one third of patients failed to attend
when appointments were offered.

The question of non-attendance is not straightforward. It may be more
appropriate to view patients as victims of the disorganisation of outpatient
care rather than as responsible for it (Frankel *et al.*, 1989). Clearly, non-
attenders represent a drain on outpatient resources, as well as preventing
others from attending. Some process of identifying patients who no longer
wish to attend could be undertaken by general practitioners, while West
and Jenkins (1984) have highlighted the importance of an indication of
the urgency of the appointment appearing on the proforma for referral.
In relation to orthopaedic outpatient appointments, the early treatment
of treatable conditions may process such patients quickly through the
system. Williams (1990) has made a similar point by recommending
prioritising patient benefits as a way of rationalising waiting lists and
allocating services.

Once patients are in the outpatient clinic there are various ways in
which the time could be better utilised to obtain maximum benefit
from the patient/consultant encounter. Instead of patients attending
hospital several times for investigations to be performed and their
results reported, outpatient sessions could be organised in such a way
that all procedures could be completed during the same day, so that a
final consultation at the end of the day would confirm the diagnosis,
and result in a course of treatment and method of follow-up. This would
require the coordination of the whole network of diagnostic services,

but would be more convenient for the patient and better for teaching purposes.

Duncan *et al.* (1988) also looked at ways of saving time in the outpatient clinic. They found that a considerable amount of consultant time was wasted on administrative details which should have been undertaken by others, such as looking for case-notes or searching for the results of investigations. The difficulties of attracting adequate numbers of permanent clerical and secretarial staff to the NHS means that temporary staff are brought in from agencies. This is obviously only a makeshift solution and results in consultants spending too much time on administrative work at the expense of seeing more outpatients.

As for the problem of discharging patients from outpatient clinics, many references have been made to the difficulties which junior doctors face, and how much easier it is to ask a patient to 'come again in six months' than to discharge him or her back to the general practitioner (Lester, 1980; Grace and Armstrong, 1987; Sparks, 1988; Jolly, 1989). However, this explanation for re-attendance was refuted by Marsh (1982) and Bosanquet *et al.* (1987), who found no difference in the probability of consultants and juniors retaining outpatients.

The relative contributions of consultants and juniors was studied by Kiff and Sykes (1988) on a sample of 4275 outpatient consultations. In general surgery less than half of the new patients, and only one third of all patients attending the clinic, were seen by a consultant. In medical clinics, just over a quarter of patients were seen by doctors who had less than six months experience in their present specialty after registration and, overall, doctors had been on continuous duty for at least twnety-four hours before a third of all consultations.

Kiff and Sykes's conclusion that the outpatient service depends heavily on incompletely trained staff who may be under stress from tiredness and volume of work, implies that more could be done by consultants, if not in terms of consultations, at least in terms of reviewing the clinic case-notes and recommending discharge. The burden of decision-making would then be taken from the junior staff (Zadik, 1976; Middleton and McHardy, 1976; Shaw, 1981; Sparks 1988). The introduction of a directive plan clipped to the front of case-notes and reviewed by the consultant prior to the clinic, as reported by Sparks (1988), resulted in a 50% reduction in follow-up appointments. Junior staff had been noted to be reluctant to discharge and were apparently happier with the introduction of such management plans.

Olsen (1976) proposed that discharge should be seen as the normal outcome of an attendance, whereas a further appointment would require a positive reason. With patients requiring long-term follow-up, he also suggested, as have others, that they should be seen by a consultant on at least every third visit, presumably in order to review the benefit of continuing follow-up (Shaw, 1981). Hall *et al.* (1988) conducted a study on the impact of introducing guidelines for follow-up arrangements and the use of diagnostic tests. They found that guidelines which specified discharge as the normal arrangement were an effective way of reducing unnecessary follow-up appointments. Ross *et al.* (1989) also reported that conducting a clinic survey resulted in a rationalisation of services and a 13% increase in the number of new appointment slots available for patients.

In addition to improving the actual rate of discharge from clinics, there have been calls to utilise alternative means for following up patients. Kirk (1976) and Howie (1977) suggested using indirect means of contact, such as letter and telephone. Hart *et al.* (1979) found that answers on prepaid reply postcards provided an efficient and realistic review of patients who had attended as day cases for urological endoscopy under general anaesthetic. However, Kirk (1976) admitted that considerable organisation and co-operation were necessary to deal with frequent letters and telephone calls, and it is debatable whether the existing administrative structures could actually cope with this additional burden (Duncan *et al.* 1988).

A recommendation from the studies which have examined general practitioner referral rates is that there should be more and better communication between consultants and general practitioners, with the aim of establishing referral guidelines. Attention has also been drawn to the inadequate and delayed nature of communications between general practitioners and consultants at referral, and between hospital and general practitioners at discharge (Forsyth and Logan, 1968; Shaw, 1981; McGlade *et al.*, 1988; Cybulska and Rucinski, 1989; Fair, 1989). It is argued that the generally poor standard of communications contributes to a lack of co-ordination in the continuing care of patients referred to and from hospital. With the additional need for agreeing guidelines for the appropriate referral of patients, regular joint discussions between consultants and general practitioners are clearly essential (Shaw, 1981; Marinker *et al.*, 1988).

The influence of the outpatients themselves

Relatively little attention has been directed to the input that outpatients themselves have on waiting lists, and the expectations that they have of the referral process. This would seem to be a rather major gap in our understanding. Various studies have involved sending questionnaires to samples of outpatients asking about such things as degree of disability sustained during waiting period, length of waiting time and reasons for non-attendance (West and McKibbin, 1982; West and Jenkins, 1984; Frankel *et al.*, 1989), and the perceptions that patients had of the reasons and appropriateness of referral (Grace and Armstrong, 1986; 1987). Sandler *et al.* (1989) asked patients to assess their satisfaction with a new information card designed to enhance consultant / patient / general practitioner communication, and McCormack *et al.* (1984) asked outpatients what they felt about follow-up at hospital and by their general practitioner.

Loudon (1976) suggested that patients are usually grateful when their general practitioner cancels an unnecessary follow-up appointment, although they are concerned that the specialist may be offended that they fail to attend. Lester (1980) noted the reassurance that patients derive from repeat outpatient attendances, while Deitch (1984) advocated more attitude surveys amongst outpatients. Priest and Lond (1962) contended that patients do not expect their doctors to make a thorough examination, but simply prescribe or refer them to hospital: 'Once having attended hospital, many patients reveal a wish to bypass their doctor from then on and show distinct reluctance to be discharged'. Stevens (1985) briefly mentioned that expectations and demands of health care by the general public have risen, and that means of influencing this demand should be sought.

These fleeting references to outpatient expectations indicate that much of what is assumed about this vast population is largely based on supposition and anecdote. That patients, with their families, can be decisive 'actors' in the discharge process seems to have been largely overlooked, although an exception is the work of Silverman and co-workers (e.g. 1987), who have looked in detail at modes of discourse within the clinic setting, particularly paediatric clinics.

It is interesting that McCormack *et al.*'s (1984) study of attitudes to follow-up revealed that only 18.9% of patients would have preferred to visit their general practitioner for follow-up after uncomplicated surgery, although the conclusions of the authors were as follows: 'Transferring the care of suitable patients to their GP would reduce the pressure on surgical out-patients and in most cases be welcomed by the GP. At present, patients expect to return to hospital following surgery, but if this were not the accepted routine, they would probably be equally happy to see their GP'.

There seems to be no evidence that the 'happiness' of patients has been of overriding concern in the past. The assertion that patients would be happy to see their general practitioner, as opposed to a hospital doctor, about a hospital procedure, begs the question of the nature of the patient / hospital doctor relationship and that between a person who is sometimes a 'patient' and his or her general practitioner. The absence of detailed research means that the question remains unanswered.

Hospital doctors and general practitioners

In comparison to the meagre work on outpatients as purposive actors embedded in specific cultural milieus, the literature on doctors is more generous (Balint, 1964; Browne and Freeling, 1976; McCormack, 1979).

Bourne (1976) described how general practitioners used referrals in many ways. Indeed, he stated that referrals affect their sense of identity and defences against anxiety. This approach, of examining the social, cultural and psychological factors which inform day-to-day decisions about particular courses of actions, would appear to be a rewarding one. To obtain a sense of the minutiae of the daily routine in the surgery, or in the outpatient clinic, might contribute a greater understanding of the way the system works (or fails to work), and the way in which the incongruity between nominal aims and reality comes about.

The expectations that general practitioners and consultants have of the other's role is fundamental to the question of outpatient activity. As we have seen, blatant conflict of interests between the two characterised the period leading up to the inception of the NHS. At the heart of the issue of how to target outpatient services is the determination of how the care of patients can best be shared between consultant and general practitioner. A key element underpining this debate is the ability of primary care services to substitute for new, repeat, or surgical follow-up outpatient attendances (Bosanquet and Fordham, 1987). Nevertheless, the decision to 'recycle' outpatients lies largely within the hospital (Shaw, 1981). The various factors, other than clinical indications, which lie behind this decision have not received sufficient attention.

The work of Kiff and Sykes (1988) is significant in that it implies that a large proportion of patients are not actually consulting consultants. Certainly when a general practitioner refers a patient for specialist advice, 'he is asking for the opinion of a consultant and not that of a junior doctor or another general practitioner disguised as a clinical assistant' (Stevens, 1985). Yet in practice it appears that fewer than one half of new referrals in medical clinics are likely to be seen by a consultant at their first visit (Kiff and Sykes, 1988), and Hopkins observed in 1976 that the numbers of new outpatients seen by consultants had declined by a median of 29% in virtually every specialty between 1963 and 1973. He found no evidence to 'encourage the belief that increasing the number of consultants will result in a more effective service to patients' (Hopkins, 1976).

The implications of this for the patient are:

> continued attendance . . . though the need for specialist care has long
> since ceased . . . They are likely to be seen by inexperienced staff who
> seldom discharge them . . . For the hospital this is a waste of time
> and resources which only results in overloaded clinics and bored
> junior staff whose single contact with the patient may have little
> meaning for either . . . The patient . . . may be exposed to apparently

conflicting advice from the various doctors he meets during his years of pilgrimage.   (Lester, 1980)

How have hospital doctors traditionally defended this system? Shaw (1981) put forward some of the reasons which are commonly mentioned: interesting cases are brought back for research, junior staff receive sound training in outpatient clinics, and there is concern that the general practitioner will not adequately follow up the patient, coupled with the idea that the hospital is relieving general practitioners of a burden. Lester (1980) pointed out that the training argument can be seen as spurious on the grounds that continuing care is better taught in the primary care setting. The justification in terms of relieving general practitioners of a burden is additionally seen as ill- informed, as these patients are also seen in general practice.

Another reason, which has already been mentioned, is that there is an inertia, perhaps borne out of overwork, where it becomes easier to ask a patient to re-attend than to institute the discharge process, which demands a more carefully considered discharge letter. Although inertia could never be defended as a pillar of good clinic management, it may easily be the most 'rational' course of action for an over-tired and over-busy, junior doctor. Concomitantly, a greater proportion of new referrals in a clinic would also add to the overall workload as a result of the investigations which would be indicated. There may therefore be powerful pressures maintaining a high proportion of re-attenders.

CONCLUSIONS

It is clear that current practice does not in general terms meet the needs of those patients awaiting specialist consultation. Indeed, the system seems to be geared to bringing back for consultation patients who have neither the clinical need nor the inclination to attend hospital, whilst blocking the way for new patients to undergo speedy assessment. This clearly represents an irrational use of resources, but to understand how this predicament has come about and how it is maintained it is necessary to consider the various steps along the decision-making way and question whether these are informed by an economic rationality, a rationality derived from other cultural values, a combination of these, or indeed are the result of a number of rather ad hoc compromises.

There are of course positive benefits that follow from long outpatient waiting lists. Williams (1990) considers two main advantages: 'Many NHS doctors supplement their incomes through private practice. Private practice flourishes in specialties and in places where waiting lists are long' and a 'second important consideration is that people have noticed that every now and again a good fairy distributes goodies to those who have exceptionally long waiting lists. These goodies consist of extra staff or other facilities hitherto denied . . . Since this is an ongoing system, if the receipt of goodies enables you to step up the work rate and make incursions into your waiting list, you had better fill it up again by ensuring that local GPs keep you well supplied with grey zone cases, otherwise private practice or future eligibility for goodies will suffer.'

Williams (1990) contends that waiting lists are composed of many patients who constitute a kind of 'grey zone', patients whose conditions are chronic and the 'judgement as to the best stage at which to treat them varies between doctors'. He suggests that these patients thus make up a kind of resource in themselves, a long waiting list being a bargaining tool for extra facilities or staff, and a pool of potential candidates for private practice. Certainly, if this is indeed the case, the situation lends itself to analyses which go beyond the conventional scope of the investigations of health service researchers and health economists. The idea that patients are routinely asked to come again in three or six months time because it is the easiest thing to do, because it maintains an aura of activity or indeed over-activity, which at the same time purposely rations the availability of new appointment slots, and which serves various consultant and departmental interests, is of course quite counter to the overt aims of the NHS. However, research is so lacking on the minutiae of decision-making in the clinic, that these explanations will have to remain speculative.

The editorial in *The Lancet* (Anonymous, 1976a), which took such a swingeing approach to outpatient follow-up, stated the core of the problem in similar terms: 'There are many reasons, apart from tradition, for continuing to write 'To come again, 3 months' in outpatient notes. Most are irrelevant to the health of the community. Few could stand up to rational examination'.

Little has changed. The scandal of the 1870s within medical circles was fired by the impact upon GPs' incomes of outpatient access to consultants. The battle lines are no longer clearly drawn, and the issue has become less controversial. The flurry of interest in outpatients since 1976 has failed to galvanise any generalised commitment to reform. The adoption of guidelines specifying criteria for GP referral and for outpatient re-attendance has been seen as a means for introducing rational change. These have been instituted by particular enthusiasts, but there is little evidence of any generalised or sustained impact.

The new contracting environment introduced under the NHS and Community Care Act (1990) offers a vehicle for incorporating criteria for outpatient attendance within the agreements between providers of hospital services and purchasing authorities or fund-holding general practices. However there is no reason to assume that the longstanding tradition of the inappropriate use of outpatient facilities will be interrupted without forceful measures to countermand the various unwitting and conscious choices that support it.

CHAPTER 6

And So to Bed: Access to Inpatient Services

Ian Harvey

The general practitioner is often spoken of as fulfilling the role of gatekeeper within the NHS. The analogy is entirely apt. As a consequence of the convention, dating back to the early part of this century, that consultants should only see non-emergency patients who have first been referred by a GP, doctors working in primary care largely control access to hospital services. It is worth re-iterating that hospital consultants can themselves greatly influence the dynamics of outpatient work by means of their own practice with regard to the follow-up of both inpatients and outpatients.

Referral behaviour (see Chapter 4) is well known to be a highly complex and variable phenomenon. Yet patients who have negotiated this daunting gateway and been referred, find themselves, like hapless airline passengers on a busy summer weekend, passing through one checkpoint, only to join another queue beyond – the hospital waiting list.

The nature of hospital waiting lists, the factors which influence them and the measures necessary to counter them form a set of problems as elusive as any in health care delivery (Deitch, 1981a). Different politicians have at various times both despaired of them (Powell, 1966) and strongly committed themselves to reducing them (Anonymous, 1987a; Dalziel and Kerr, 1987) and the media clearly regard the issue as newsworthy (Laurance, 1988; Hildrew, 1987). The following comments will strike a chord amongst many who have examined the issue: 'With so much advice on a chronic and apparently unremitting problem the cynic might be forgiven for calling to mind the clinical dictum which suggests that the greater the number of remedies for a particular condition the less the likelihood that any is really effective.' (Morris, 1984).

In this chapter I intend to consider issues surrounding the measurement of waiting for inpatient care and factors which may be responsible for the variation in waiting lists in this country. I shall devote some time to a detailed analysis of those factors which may 'cause' waiting lists and

96

relate these to the 'irrational' use of resources, before concluding with a new concept of the problem, based firmly on its multifactorial nature.

HOSPITAL WAITING LISTS – WHAT DO THEY MEASURE?

There is much to be gained from a simple account of what actually happens to a referral from a GP once it reaches hospital. Upon receipt of a referral letter the patient joins the outpatient waiting list. If a particular consultant has been specified in the referral letter then the patient joins that list. If not, the patient joins a general waiting list, from which patients are allocated to consultants.

National data are not collected on the length of outpatient waiting lists, although such data are often collected locally. If, after being seen by the consultant, admission is deemed necessary, the patient joins the inpatient waiting list. National figures on these are available. However certain categories of patient are specifically excluded from these statistics, including patients whose admissions have been deferred because, for example, an offered date for admission was inconvenient or because the condition did not require treatment until a later date. Until 1987 patients awaiting day surgery were also excluded (Mordue, 1989) and patients returning for regular check procedures (for example, cystoscopies) still are. Booked admissions, where a date for admission has been agreed at the time of the outpatient consultation, are included in the statistics.

Two issues arise from this. First, what exactly is a waiting list meant to measure? One possible view is that it aims to measure the number of individuals who are currently experiencing a level of medical need sufficient to warrant admission to hospital, but whose admission is, for organisational reasons, not immediately possible. Some of the exclusions from inpatient waiting list statistics strongly suggest that such a concept underlies the present definition. It is consistent with this concept to exclude patients returning regularly to hospital for certain procedures, such as check cystoscopies or colonoscopies. It is less obvious, however, why patients awaiting day surgery should have been completely omitted until comparatively recently, and are still not disaggregated to the same extent as others awaiting inpatient treatment in English waiting list publications. Day surgery has become more common as a result of advances in anaesthetic agents, combined with pressure on limited resources, rather than a decline in the level of need of the patients. It will undoubtedly become even more common. It seems illogical, as others have commented (Morris, 1984), to deal differently with such patients merely because their conditions are amenable to day case procedures.

The second issue has to do with the clarity of definition of these various categories of patient. There is, for example, obvious potential ambiguity surrounding the distinction between a booked and a deferred admission. Furthermore, there is good reason to believe that some at least of those clerical staff collecting the data are uncertain about what exactly ought to be counted. Although patients whose admissions have been postponed at their own request should be omitted, according to current definitions, (although one may debate the appropriateness of this), they are erroneously included in waiting list returns in many localities. Thus, although a waiting list approximates to the number of people experiencing a degree of need warranting admission but whose need remains unmet, its margins are blurred. The contribution of this lack of clarity to the variation that is observed in waiting list lengths is unknown, but provides some cause for concern. Although sniping at the quality of data can be a mere distraction, nonetheless the problem cannot be ignored.

SHOULD WE BE MEASURING THE LENGTHS OF WAITING LISTS AT ALL?

It is undeniable that, to quote one writer: 'hospital waiting lists will always be used as yard-sticks with which to measure . . . efficiency' (White, 1980). Others have pointed out, however, that the length of a waiting list does not automatically reflect the quantity of underlying interest – the length of time that will be spent on that list (Williams *et al.*, 1983; Deitch, 1981b). It is theoretically possible to envisage a situation in which a shorter time is spent waiting in a long queue than is spent in a short queue. To cope with this objection limited information is now collected on both inpatient waiting times (in the form of the proportion of non-urgent cases waiting for longer than one year and the proportion of urgent cases waiting longer than one month) and outpatient waiting (in the form of the proportion waiting longer than three months).

There is however a further problem. The waiting list does not function like a simple queue (see Chapter 3), with patients joining at one end, waiting in line and leaving at the other. To begin with it contains cases of varying severity, the more urgent of whom can expect to pass more quickly through the system, leaving behind a residual number who may move forward only very slowly, if at all. Information about the time spent waiting by those on the waiting list therefore gives a biased and pessimistic estimate of the waiting experience of the total group placed on the waiting list. Conversely, the waiting times of those admitted to hospital from the waiting list is biased in the opposite direction. This distinction is conceptually analogous to that drawn between prevalence and incidence in epidemiology (Don *et al.*, 1987).

One possible way around this difficulty is to look at the notional time required to clear the waiting list. Mathematically this is represented by the expression:

Notional waiting time (yrs) = Number of patients on waiting list
÷ Discharges and deaths from waiting list per year

This measure has been advocated as a summary of average waiting experience that may be anticipated by individuals about to join a waiting list (Cottrell, 1980). As such, however, it gives no indication of the degree of variation in individual waiting times, nor of the shape of that distribution. Others have argued that what is properly required is the measurement of the waiting times of a cohort of individuals placed on the waiting list and followed until all have been admitted (Mason, 1976). This has been described and attempted in at least one study (Williams *et al.*, 1983).

Yates (1987), however, has strongly asserted that there is an unmistakable association between waiting list length and waiting times and that the distinction between the two represents a distraction from the central problem. He comments that: 'Those who point out that there is not necessarily a connection between waiting numbers and waiting times do themselves and the public a great disservice'. He advances a compelling intuitive argument that we should judge long hospital waiting lists as we judge long supermarket queues – by deducing that the longer the queue the longer the wait.

Such an assertion is considerably strengthened if supporting data are available and a recent study using English data on trauma and orthopaedic waiting lists supports Yates' view to some extent (Harley, 1988). This reported a correlation of 0.5 between waiting list length and waiting time – a relationship described, however, as 'not strong'. Perhaps, as Cottrell (1980) has suggested, it is inappropriate to look at the crude length of a waiting list without standardising for the size of population which generated that list. This argues in favour of describing waiting list length as the number waiting per unit catchment population and is comparable, to extend Yates' original analogy, to considering the length of a supermarket queue in relation to the number of people in the store.

A re-examination of Yates' hypothesis is therefore appropriate, using this more refined measure of waiting list length. A crude test of this hypothesis may be performed, using 1988 inpatient data for the health districts of Wales. A crude summary measure of waiting time may be derived from the mean of two proportions – the proportion of urgent cases waiting for longer than one month and the proportion of non-urgent cases waiting for longer than one year. If this is then plotted against the total waiting list length per 100 000 catchment population for the nine Welsh health districts, the correlation coefficient is 0.745, which is significant at the 5% level. A modification of Yates' assertion therefore receives a degree of empirical support – the length of a waiting list per unit catchment population does indeed appear to give some general indication of the waiting experience of those on it.

VARIATION IN WAITING LISTS

Having suggested that the length of a waiting list is a quantity of some interest (other than purely political), the next issue to discuss is variation in waiting lists. The existence of marked variation in lengths of waiting lists is well documented (College of Health, 1987; Anonymous, 1985). It is seen at all levels of aggregation of data, from international comparisons to inter-surgeon comparisons. For epidemiologists and statisticians, however, this variation provides the base from which to proceed to test hypotheses and investigate factors which may be important in the aetiology of waiting lists. This may in turn suggest practical strategies for the reduction of waiting times and lengths.

WHAT CAUSES WAITING LISTS?

Inadequate resources

One obvious and popular explanation for waiting lists, not least amongst health workers, is in terms of a mismatch in the balance between health care provision and demand. This account views long waiting lists as resulting from inadequate resources. Yet what is the evidence for or against this view?

At an international level it is often stated that in countries such as America and West Germany, whose level of spending on health is higher than our own, both in absolute terms and in terms of proportion of gross domestic product, waiting lists are not encountered. Before examining this issue in more detail it should be pointed out that such comparisons are potentially confounded by differences in methods of health care funding and delivery, in addition to differences in the level of funding.

Within the United Kingdom relatively few studies have examined the relationship between resource levels and waiting lists, doubly surprising in view of the strong views frequently expressed both for and against this particular hypothesis. At the simplest level, the tendency for the national waiting list to lengthen at times of industrial disruption has often been invoked in support of the intuitively obvious idea that a decline in health service activity leads to a lengthening of waiting lists. The more rigorous evidence that is available approaches the issue from each of two broad directions. Some studies take a narrow view of resources and consider mainly the relation between medical manpower levels and waiting lists, whilst ignoring the important influence of nurses, beds and theatres (Fowkes *et al.*, 1983). Others look at patient throughput as a proxy for resource levels. All of them force us to examine our intuitions more closely.

Time-trend data for both inpatient waiting lists and surgical manpower reveal that, despite a 46% increase in the number of surgeons in England and Wales between 1959 and 1976, the aggregate waiting list for surgery increased by 43% in the same period. The size of the average waiting list per surgeon remained remarkably constant at 145 (Buttery and Snaith, 1979; Frost, 1980) However, a whole host of other changes have occurred in the same period, in terms of technical surgical capabilities, referral practice and patients' expectations and so this evidence is difficult to interpret. Cross sectional data will tend to control for these factors and is therefore probably more illuminating.

Buttery and Snaith (1980) examined the correlation between the number of surgeons per 100 000 population and the length of waiting list per 100 000 population, using cross sectional data from the English health regions for 1977. They found a negative correlation (−0.29) between these variables. That is, more surgeons were associated with shorter waiting lists, both quantities having been standardised for size of population served. However, this correlation was not statistically significant. There are, since the work is based upon regional data, only fourteen data points and it would be informative to see the work repeated at a lower level of aggregation. It is possible to re-work the Regional data in Buttery and Snaith's paper, and use simple linear regression to relate the length of waiting list per 100 000 to the number of surgeons per 100 000. One can then extrapolate to calculate the number of surgeons required to give a zero waiting list. The figure arrived at is 13.2 per 100 000, or two and a half times the UK complement. Fascinatingly, this is broadly similar to the surgical manpower levels found in countries such as West Germany or the United States, where waiting lists are claimed not to exist (Schroeder, 1984; Bunker, 1970; Commission on the provision of surgical services, 1986). Extrapolating in this way is fraught with hazards, but, nonetheless provides some tenuous support for the notion that an increase in surgical manpower to levels similar to those found in some other countries might achieve a reduction in, or even abolition of, waiting lists.

Harley (1988) has adopted the second broad approach of using throughput as a proxy for resource levels. This study compared the characteristics of thirty UK health districts with long trauma and orthopaedic waiting lists with other districts. A significant negative association was found between waiting time (expressed as Notional Waiting Time) and the number of deaths and discharges per unit population. There was also a positive association between waiting time and average length of stay. If one accepts that throughput is governed, not solely, but at least in part, by resources, then this evidence again suggests that an increase in health service resources (and hence activity and throughput) might reduce waiting times and lists. .

These fragments of evidence offer some hope that the waiting list problem may not be completely insoluble. However, lying diametrically opposed to this is the axiom that the need for health care is effectively infinite and that any increase in health care provision simply stimulates further demand in the absence of any pricing mechanism to discourage it (Cullis and Jones, 1983; Jones and McCarthy, 1978; Frost and Francis, 1979). This view asserts that, as we work away at melting the iceberg of medical demand, so more of it bobs relentlessly to the surface. Although the concept of infinite demand for surgical procedures has been challenged on theoretical grounds (Anonymous, 1987b), this notion, if correct, has the most profoundly pessimistic implications for efforts to reduce waiting lists.

The growth in national waiting lists, despite the growth in numbers of surgeons, has already been mentioned (Buttery and Snaith, 1979). A recent careful analysis of ten years data from the Oxford Region has also found a statistically significant positive correlation between the number of admissions from surgical waiting lists and the length of those lists (Goldacre *et al.*, 1987). In other words, an increase in throughput was associated with an increase in waiting lists. This observation was contrary to the investigators' prior expectation and one possible explanation they propose is that previously unmet need is being translated into demand. However, their more detailed analysis calls into question this simple explanation. They discovered that a change in the length of waiting lists was significantly associated with a change in the same direction in the number of admissions in the following quarter. In other words, the increase in length of lists preceded the increase in throughput. This suggests that unknown factors may alter the length of the waiting list, which then permits or stimulates in some way a change in throughput. One may perhaps reasonably infer that, if an increase in throughput could be achieved without a preceding increase in waiting list length, waiting lists could in fact decrease.

The relationship between resources (and hence throughput) on the one hand, and waiting list length and waiting times on the other, is inadequately researched and remains unresolved. Many are forced to take the cautious view adopted by, for example, Coulter and McPherson (1987) that an increase in throughput has the potential for producing a reduction in waiting times, but qualified by an appreciation that the relation is not a simple one.

Artefact

As has already been briefly discussed, waiting list definitions contain certain ambiguities, especially with regard to deferred cases. It seems entirely plausible to attempt to account for at least some of the variation in inter-hospital and inter-District waiting lists in terms of different counting procedures. There are, for example, differences in coping with patients who have been offered an admission date and have declined it, or patients who are returning for check procedures such as cystoscopies. Officially these patients should be excluded, but some Districts are known to include them.

Furthermore, the routinely published inpatient waiting list statistics for English Health Districts (but not Regions) specifically exclude day cases, an omission which might easily lead to spurious differences between Districts and hospitals with extensive facilities for day surgery and those without. Some idea of the possible magnitude of this effect is given in a study from Manchester which looked at the waiting lists of ten surgeons from a range of specialties (Sykes, 1986). Here it was found that 325 out of 1094 patients awaiting surgery were in fact day cases, and would not appear in Department of Health routine District waiting list statistics. In another District, without such facilities, these patients would appear.

A further element in the artefact argument is that waiting lists frequently contain patients who have died, or received their treatment elsewhere (or even within the same hospital) and have simply not been removed from the list. It might be that some Districts or hospitals are more efficient at reviewing and up-dating their lists. Again evidence is available as to the number of patients inappropriately retained on particular waiting lists.

Lee and colleagues (1987) have presented evidence suggesting that overall waiting lists may be inflated by as much as 28%. Donaldson and colleagues (1984) studied the combined waiting lists of eight orthopaedic surgeons working in a single District General Hospital in Leicester. They found that of 950 patients who had been waiting for admission for more than one year, 193 (20%) had already been operated on within the same hospital and a further 65 (7%) had been operated on elsewhere. Others have reported similar findings (Lourie, 1978; Porter, 1985). It is worth noting in passing that with the advent of computerised Patient Administration Systems, such oversights should in principle become less common, although West's experiences (see Chapter 3) were not very encouraging.

An additional element in the Leicester study described above (Donaldson *et al.*, 1984) involved writing to all those on the waiting list asking if they wished to remain on the list. Only 38% of the group indicated that they still wished to be operated upon, although it would be mistaken to infer from this that the need for surgery had been resolved in all these patients – it may simply be that legitimate demand had been suppressed by a long wait. By contrast West and McKibbin (1982), in a similar study of those on an orthopaedic outpatient waiting list, found that a much lower percentage – between 11% and 13% – felt that their problem had resolved spontaneously whilst they had been on the waiting list and therefore no longer wished to be seen.

However, the central issue at stake – namely the extent to which variations in waiting lists may be accounted for by artefacts – remains uncertain. Although the Leicester figures provide, for one specialty, an estimate of the number of waiting list cases who should have been removed from the list, there is no evidence as to the degree of systematic variation in this administrative inefficiency.

The potential problems of ambiguity, exclusion and out-datedness in waiting list statistics are of sufficient magnitude, when aggregated, to cause concern about the validity of the data. Nonetheless, there can be few who doubt that, even when these factors are taken into account, startling variation remains, particularly between individual consultants.

A variant of the artefact explanation is proposed in a fascinating paper by Sanderson (1982), which draws upon the example of cataract surgery. He suggests that inter-surgeon variation in waiting list length may result simply from a tendency of some surgeons to place patients on the waiting list earlier in the natural history of their illness than other surgeons, thereby generating longer waiting lists. There is unfortunately no evidence presented, however, to support this notion of varying thresholds for waiting list entry.

Nonetheless, it is both plausible and simple, and it leads Sanderson to conclude that adequacy of resources is not a direct influence on waiting list length. He argues, indeed, that attempts to clear waiting lists by introducing day surgery or redeploying beds or manpower may, paradoxically, result in the performance of unnecessary surgery as the operative threshold is lowered. This is an issue to which I shall return below.

The distorting influence of private practice

Several contributors to this volume have already indicated the importance of a consideration of the impact of private practice, from its historical beginnings (Chapter 4) to modern times (Chapter 3; Chapter 5).

The role of private practice in the aetiology of waiting lists is hotly disputed. One approach has been to argue that the private route has a beneficial influence, by decanting patients away from NHS waiting lists, which would otherwise be longer. Another view holds that the fact that all NHS consultants, regardless of the contract they hold, are now permitted to undertake a certain amount of private work spreads a perverse incentive throughout hospital practice with regard to waiting list management. The perception that a long wait will result if treatment is pursued within the NHS is undoubtedly a factor encouraging patients to seek private treatment (Bayliss, 1988; Higgins, 1988), along with other elements such as greater flexibility of admission time and superior hotel facilities. By maintaining a long NHS waiting list, this second argument runs, an individual surgeon stimulates private practice. Yet a third view is that longer waiting lists are the result of the time that surgeons spend in the private sector – in other words, that waiting lists lengthen secondarily to private practice rather than being cultivated (more or less consciously) as a means of enhancing private business.

Different authors inevitably take varying views of the importance that they attach to private practice in the genesis of waiting lists. Yates (1987) comments that: 'He (the consultant) has a financial incentive to be inefficient' and plainly feels that it is a significant factor in at least some localities. Others argue that it is the quality of NHS treatment offered by the individual clinician that attracts private work; thus maintaining a long NHS list may be interpreted as indicating inefficiency and hence be counterproductive (Lewis, 1981). This latter interpretation seems excessively convoluted. Moreover it fails to take account of the recent tendency for health authorities, rather than individual consumers, to bulk purchase private operations – generally in local private hospitals – in an attempt to clear the long waiting lists of the very clinicians who are performing the private operations (Deitch, 1985). The Duthie Report (1981) into orthopaedic services found no evidence of a significant impact of private practice upon NHS waiting times in either direction, however, although the volume of private surgery has undoubtedly increased since its publication (McPherson *et al.*, 1985a).

Virtually no published empirical work has addressed this particular issue. I have however performed a simple analysis of the waiting lists (inpatient and outpatient combined) of two small groups of general surgeons, one composed of six individuals undertaking no private practice and the other of seven surgeons with at least some private practice. This shows that the private practitioners had statistically significantly longer waiting lists (no private practice, median waiting list = 111; private practice, median waiting list = 286. $p = 0.02$, Mann Whitney test). Such small scale data provide only a broad indication and of course cannot determine the directionality of the relationship.

Nonetheless, they suggest that in the private practice issue there exists a suitable subject for more detailed empirical work, to raise the level of debate above the merely speculative and anecdotal.

Irrational practice

In view of the fact that the title of this book is *Rationing and Rationality in the NHS* it is inevitable that one should eventually consider a set of explanations for waiting lists which invoke the concept of irrational use of existing levels of resources. Before considering the specific nature of the relationship between waiting lists and irrational resource use, it is worthwhile considering, in more general terms, the extent to which clinical (especially surgical) practice may be considered to be rational – that is governed by reason, or cogent argument (see also Chapter 1).

RATIONAL MEDICINE? A DIGRESSION

To illustrate this issue it is instructive to consider the profound differences that exist, even between apparently similar European countries, in the recognition and nomenclature of medical disorders. In Germany, for example, low blood pressure is regarded as an illness requiring medical attention; the consultation rate for this is 163 per million per year and 85 drugs are available for its treatment. In Britain, by contrast, no such condition is recognised (Clare, 1989). There is strong evidence, indeed, that most, if not all, clinical practice is a culture-bound phenomenon, guided as much by deeply rooted traditions and ideas as by neutral scientific values and empirical findings (Payer, 1988). Doctors may delight in their professional autonomy, personal idiosyncrasies and clinical freedom, but even they must be surprised by the degree of variation in clinical practice at the level of both societies and individuals.

The problem of waiting lists is mainly a problem of the surgical specialties. There is a large literature that focuses upon variation in surgical practice, especially between nations with different methods of financing health care delivery. Underpinning much of the interpretation and discussion of this evidence is a normative view (in practice more honoured in the breach than in the observance) that a rational health care system should provide demonstrably effective treatment to those who will benefit at a cost acceptable to that society. The terminology I have used here is, of course, not value-free; what, for example, constitutes a benefit, what must a treatment achieve in order to be considered effective, and what is an acceptable cost? It is instructive nevertheless to pause for a moment to consider how closely medical practice corresponds, even to this imperfectly defined rational model.

There is a startling degree of variation, both between and within countries, in the rate at which certain common operations are performed and, indeed, in the types of operation performed for common conditions (Andersen and Mooney, 1990; Gazet *et al.*, 1985). Moreover, these are surgical procedures for which many lay people could be forgiven for believing there are widely agreed indications. Among the first to comment on this was Glover (1948) when reporting the wide variation in the rate at which tonsillectomy was performed on children in Kent. She also highlighted some of the ambiguities surrounding the deceptively simple indications – such as the presence of 'obviously diseased tonsils' – for this procedure. Many investigators, examining the international variation in the incidence of operations such as tonsillectomy, inguinal herniorrhaphy and cholecystectomy, have concluded that supply factors (numbers of surgeons and beds), an interventionist surgical philosophy and financial incentives based on fee-for- service, coupled with insurance reimbursement, all tend to produce high rates of operations, over and above any underlying differences in morbidity, and may well be the dominant factors (Bunker, 1970; Vayda, 1973; Pearson *et al.*, 1968).

Similar findings have been reported from more detailed studies based on less aggregated data from individual countries (Lewis, 1969; Roos and Roos, 1982; Wennberg, 1987a). Indeed there is clear evidence that the relationship between surgical rates and underlying morbidity levels is at best a tenuous one. In one Canadian study, for example, no relationship was found between morbidity levels (measured using standardised interview techniques) amongst a random sample of elderly people and elective surgical rates (Roos and Roos, 1982). This has been adduced as evidence against what has been termed the 'needs model' of surgical practice, a model which would tend to predict a close correlation between morbidity and operative rates.

In only a relatively few instances indeed has a clear relationship emerged between underlying morbidity and surgical intervention. One such study found a close correlation between post mortem prevalence of gallstones and cholecystectomy rates within the United Kingdom (McPherson *et al.*, 1985b). The authors pointed out, however, that cholecystectomy is relatively unusual in being a procedure for which, within particular medical cultures, there appear to be reasonably uniform indications and hence consistency of use. Furthermore, they agreed with other authors that the marked international variation in cholecystectomy rates, which are unrelated to underlying morbidity differences, probably reflect wide medico-cultural differences in the setting of operative thresholds.

As with all demonstrations of variation in medical practice, whether it be prescribing habits, referral practice or intervention rates, the ever-present temptation is to assume that the higher rates are wasteful and undesirable and the lower rates the more appropriate (Goran, 1979). Many have rightly cautioned that it is impossible even to begin to pronounce on this matter in the absence of data on benefits and costs, measured in the context of randomised controlled trials (Chassin *et al.*, 1986; Roos and Roos, 1982; McPherson *et al.*, 1985b; Wennberg, 1987a). Inspection of the variation alone does not resolve the problem of whether low rates leave readily treatable morbidity untreated, or whether high rates involve inflicting unnecessary surgery without hope of overall benefit (Wennberg *et al.*, 1987b).

The aggregated behaviour of surgeons would appear, therefore, from the evidence discussed, to be profoundly irrational. Individually, how-ever, surgeons tend to be more consistent. They appear to be guided in their decision making by a relatively constant set of criteria (McPherson *et al.*, 1981). Their internal consistency and, hence, individual rationality, is unfortunately largely negated by the absence of a wider rationality rooted firmly in the systematic evaluation of benefits and costs.

Putting to one side the influences upon operative rates of underlying morbidity and of supply variables, such as surgeons and beds, there is also strong evidence that surgeons are inherently less certain about the indica-tions for certain operations, such as hysterectomy, haemorrhoidectomy, tonsillectomy and prostatectomy, than they are for other procedures, such as appendicectomy and inguinal herniorrhaphy (McPherson *et al.*, 1982; Coulter and McPherson, 1986) Moreover the same pattern of uncertainty recurs in countries with markedly different health systems.

Wennberg has identified a similar phenomenon (Wennberg and Gittel-sohn, 1982; Wennberg, 1988) and has coined the graphic term 'surgical signature' to describe the distinctive pattern of practice, found within any small geographical area, that results from the combined judgements and preferences – in other words the practice style (Wennberg, 1985) – of the individual surgeons working there. Each small group of surgeons tends to have its own 'surgical signature'. Empirical support for the influence of 'practice style' upon hysterectomy rates comes from a Canadian study which identified hysterectomy-prone physicians (Roos, 1984).

It is also interesting that the procedures which show the most variation – hysterectomy and tonsillectomy in particular – are those about which there is least information concerning risks and benefits (Wennberg and Gittelsohn, 1982). It would be mistaken, however, to conclude that the benefits of operations which show lesser degrees of variation must therefore be proven beyond doubt. Cholecystectomy is a good example of a procedure whose rates show relatively little variation attributable to individual surgeons' preferences, but the indications and benefits, especially in the treatment of flatulent dyspepsia, remain highly controversial (Anonymous, 1988a; Wennberg *et al.*, 1980). Simply because clinicians show relative consistency in their practice does not mean that this is necessarily the result of the availability of sound evidence.

To a certain extent the 'surgical signature' concept remains controversial (Pauly, 1979). It has been proposed that if 'practice style' is an important factor, then it follows that clinicians with high intervention rates should manifest lower thresholds for intervention. This prediction has been put to the test in several studies with equivocal results. Some have shown no evidence of lower thresholds in high utilisation areas (Roos *et al.*, 1977; Chassin, 1987a) and have helped to sustain the argument that there exists a large reservoir of patients with entirely appropriate indications whose needs are going unmet. Other studies, on the other hand, have supported the prediction (Chassin *et al.*, 1987b; Brook *et al.*, 1988).

Intuitively the 'surgical signature' concept provides an elegant and plausible explanation for variation. Yet it would be naive to expect the observed variation in intervention rates to be unifactorial. There are plainly many influences at work – variation in morbidity, in supply of surgical facilities and staff, in the expectations of patients (Domenighetti *et al.*, 1988), in the nature of the financial incentives operating in particular countries, as well as in the individual preferences of practitioners (Morgan *et al.*, 1987a; Anonymous, 1988b).

Nor is the overall rate at which surgical procedures are performed the only example of variation that is of interest. Variation in length of hospital stay, for example, raises precisely the same set of questions and issues regarding its aetiology (Morgan, 1988; Morgan *et al.*, 1987b). Several studies have examined in detail the possible causal factors determining length of stay and have pointed towards a major role both for technological developments (Sloan and Valvona, 1986) and for specific aspects of hospital organisation (Griffiths *et al.*, 1979; Eastaugh, 1980).

To summarise, a fundamental impediment to the pursuit of rational medicine remains the dissociation that exists between daily medical practice and the (admittedly sparse) evidence from outcome evaluations (Wennberg *et al.*, 1980; Cochrane, 1972). Doctors have on occasion shown themselves willing to be influenced by epidemiologically sound research – as regards, for example, appropriate lengths of stay (Morris *et al.*, 1968; Adler *et al.*, 1978) – but in other instances they have been notably reluctant to alter established patterns of practice (Mather *et al.*, 1971; Hill *et al.*, 1978).

There remains a pressing need both to evaluate current clinical policies and develop effective methods of influencing clinical behaviour in the light of the results obtained (Eddy, 1984).

Irrational practice and waiting lists

Irrationality, I would propose, plays a crucial role both in the genesis of waiting lists and in the way we habitually think about and analyse the waiting list problem. Conventionally the magnitude of this problem is conceptualised in terms of its length or, more recently, in terms of waiting times. However, such thinking omits several crucial steps which form part of a logical appreciation of the problem and so leads to a neglect of some of the strategies available to tackle it.

It is not the existence alone of a waiting list that is important, nor even the fact that, whilst on the waiting list, the patient may be experiencing pain or disability. Waiting lists matter only if they contain patients whose quality or length of life could be improved by the medical intervention they are awaiting (Bloom and Fendrick, 1987), and long waiting lists matter more than short, only if they contain more of these patients. The corollary of this is that patients whose lives will be rendered more miserable and, quite possibly, shorter by the proposed treatment (and such treatments do exist) are better off remaining in the queue. For them a waiting list is an asset.

However, waiting lists are unequivocally irrational if and when they develop into repositories of patients for whom, in aggregate, considerably greater health improvements could be obtained (within the same resource constraints) than are in fact currently obtained for those patients given priority in hospital admission policies. In other words, waiting lists offend against rational principles most profoundly when their composition is the result of inefficient (in the true economic sense of the word) practice (Williams and Anderson, 1975).

To what extent is this the case? What evidence is there that waiting lists contain an abundance of patients for whom much could be done, and that actual hospital admissions are biased towards patients (often interesting to doctors and medical students) for whom relatively little can be done?

One of the many frustrations about the study of waiting lists is the absence of routinely available relevant data. Until the recent advent of waiting list modules of the more advanced computerised Patient Administration Systems (PAS) it has been impossible routinely to determine the medical problems for which patients on waiting lists are awaiting admission. A recent *ad hoc* study of long inpatient lists in ten health districts has confirmed the suspicion, however, that a few conditions – hernias, varicose veins, cataract, tonsils and adenoids, arthroscopy and sterilisation – account for a disproportionately large number of those waiting (Davidge *et al.*, 1987). Clues as to why these particular conditions should feature so prominently can be found, perhaps, in statements such as this: 'It seems that we are less willing than our forefathers to tolerate minor ailments and cosmetically unsatisfactory conditions such as varicose veins and hernias' (Anonymous, 1972). One surgeon has commented that consultants often seem least interested in the most common conditions presenting to them (Jennett, 1987), a fact also suggested by Table 1.3 in Chapter 1.

Is the archetypal surgeon's perception of these problems as trivial an accurate one? In one sense, yes – there is no doubt that the adverse effects upon health of carcinoma of the pancreas are immeasurably greater than those of an inguinal hernia, for example, although the morbidity associated with the common waiting list conditions is by no means negligible (West and Jenkins, 1984). However, the central objective, I would suggest, of rational medical practice is to relieve suffering and prolong life. Is there not in fact far more scope for achieving this by diverting attention and resources away from the life-threatening, but irremediable, towards the merely disabling, but curable (West, Frankel and Roberts 1981) ?

At this point the empirical foundation for the competing views on this issue becomes sparse. Inter-treatment comparisons of costs and benefits, with benefits measured in some common unit, such as Quality Adjusted LifeYears(seeChapter2),aresimplynotwidelyavailable.Nonethelessaviewis gradually gaining prominence that surgical intervention in certain groups of patients who currently receive relatively high priority may well be wasteful (Jennett, 1987; Stoll, 1988; Joensuu *et al.*, 1989; Fitzpatrick *et al.*, 1977; Bendixen, 1977). There are almost certainly surgical procedures in current use waiting to join the list of discarded operations – those for visceral ptosis, constipation and, perhaps most notoriously, internal mammary artery ligation for angina – which are now of only historical interest, but which in their time were believed effective.

If a strategy of surgical substitution is to be recommended, evidence is required of the effectiveness of surgery for the common waiting list conditions. Even here, where it appears to many abundantly clear that a simple operation promises easy relief, there is not universal agreement (Wennberg *et al.*, 1980). The role of surgical intervention in the treatment of varicose veins is controversial in the light of the effective alternative of sclerotherapy (Chant *et al.*, 1972). The place of herniorrhaphy in the elderly is disputed (Neuhauser, 1977), and reservations have been expressed about the broad selection criteria for cataract surgery (Jaffe, 1978). Any solution to the waiting list problem must take note of and resolve these residual uncertainties or risk appearing as irrational as the practice which it seeks to replace. Nonetheless there can be relatively little doubt that, in terms of costs and benefits, the common waiting list conditions, whether definitively treated surgically or more conservatively, represent good 'value for money'.

Towards a new concept of the waiting list problem

The 'nightmare scenario' of the health economists holds, as we have discussed, that, because the demand for health care is infinite, it follows that any increase in resources or throughput, far from reducing waiting lists, will stimulate additional demand and, in a homoeostatic fashion, waiting list lengths will be maintained. Of the evidence which has been adduced, some supports this view, whilst other studies suggest that this may not necessarily hold within particular health care systems at particular points in time. Currently this controversy is in the nature of a quasi-theological argument, conducted in isolation from any adequately controlled empirical studies.

Even if one believes (as I personally do) that additional resources would in their aggregate effect produce a reduction in global waiting list length, there remains the problem that this is a solution with an emphatic political dimension. The containment of total health spending at or below current levels is a priority for many governments and even the most ardent advocate of additional resources for health services must acknowledge that the cost effectiveness of an expansionist strategy is by no means self-evident.

In the short term, therefore, the waiting list as a rationing mechanism will almost certainly remain in a health system, such as that in the UK, which is free at the point of access. The duty which rests upon the medical profession is to ensure that, within the available resources, the greatest possible health benefit is obtained for the population. A truly optimal solution is unlikely to be acceptable, even if attainable, because of the need for the competing consideration of equity (as between different age/sex groups, ethnic groups and geographical areas) to be taken into account.

Nonetheless, cost effectiveness considerations should enter into all resource allocation decisions within the medical sphere. Whether this would reduce waiting lists or times or whether more of the clinical iceberg of unmet need would simply float to the surface remains uncertain, but in some respect this is irrelevant. The health gain improvement for the population is an adequate objective in itself.

What is the scope then for improving the level of health benefits while remaining broadly within existing resource constraints? In aggregate terms the total health benefit obtained for the whole population is the product of the average benefit per patient and the number of patients passing through the health system. We may further constrain this model by stipulating that the total expenditure on health should remain roughly constant.

With regard to the second of these factors, there is substantial evidence that more patients could be catered for by a combination of organisational changes and changes in medical attitudes, which would have only modest (but nonetheless some) resource implications (Anonymous, 1987b). This evidence exists across a wide range of activities, from wasteful use of consultant time in outpatients (Duncan *et al.*, 1988) to inappropriate occupation of acute beds (Anderson *et al.*, 1988; Coid and Crome, 1986) and less than optimal use of available theatre time (Barr *et al.*, 1982; National Audit Office, 1987).

Moreover these problems are capable of resolution. There is experimental evidence that regular review of inpatients, according to predetermined criteria, can reduce the proportion of beds inappropriately occupied, without any increase in morbidity or mortality (Mozes *et al.*, 1987). There is additional evidence that organisational and managerial measures, such as the introduction of a bed manager, can have a considerable impact on throughput and, indeed, waiting list lengths, at no or relatively low additional cost (Southam and Talbot, 1980; Heppenstall, 1985; Payne *et al.*, 1987). Changes in surgical practice patterns, including an extension of day surgery and of surgery under local anaesthesia, have also been reported to reduce long waiting lists (Ogg and Obey, 1987; Lakhani *et al.*, 1987; Morris and Jarrett, 1987; Bishop and Jarrett, 1986).

Underpining many of these strategies is a policy of bringing the resources essential to surgical practice – surgical and nursing manpower, beds and theatre time – into a better balance. A study of one specialty (ENT surgery) in Wales has suggested that, when it is surgical manpower that is the limiting factor, recruiting more junior staff, rather than more consultant staff, is likely to produce greater throughput (West *et al.*, 1988).

The second factor contributing to the overall health benefit of the population is the average benefit obtained per patient. Here I have argued that there is strong reason to believe that the waiting list conditions – which in effect tend to be selectively ignored- are extremely cost-effective conditions to treat, having a high ratio of benefit to cost. The controversy surrounding the recent White Paper on the NHS (Secretary of State for Health, 1989) has obscured one of its less disputed recommendations – the establishment of treatment centres specialising in the common waiting list conditions. It is the intention that such a 'dedicated' facility may overcome the apparent lack of interest in certain conditions.

CONCLUSION

I have attempted in this chapter to delineate some of the controversies surrounding inpatient waiting lists, and the relation between waiting list length and waiting times and various hypothesised causal factors. It is a truism to say that the phenomenon is multifactorial. What cannot sensibly be commented upon in the current state of knowledge is the relative importance of the various factors.

I have also argued that an excessive concentration upon the superficial meaning of waiting lists and times, in terms simply of their magnitude, ignores the more fundamental aspects of the problem they actually symbolise. This is the existence of unmet and remediable need for which, putting to one side some residual but important uncertainties, cheap and easy (but, to surgeons, unattractive) procedures exist. The apparent irrationality and economic inefficiency represented by this phenomenon merely reflects the multiplicity of factors, few of them within the realms of pure scientific endeavour, which actually determine medical practice. A further element in my approach has been a pragmatic acceptance of the difficulties of achieving greater levels of public health expenditure in most western countries, even if the relationship between waiting list and resource levels were beyond dispute.

Pleas for rationality in determining the pattern of medical practice have a long and honourable pedigree. Sceptics argue that the methods of quantification of health benefits necessary for evaluative research are so crude that more subtle aspects of the patient's experience are lost. This argues for the primacy of the clinical impression, which relates in turn to a view of medicine as being as much an art as a science. Yet medical practice has already, to a considerable extent, incorporated rigorous evaluative methodologies – many clinicians, for example, participate in randomised controlled trials. The waiting list problem represents, in many respects, a failure of evidence to be translated into practice, and is the exact counterpart within the medical sphere of the gap, well known to psychologists, between knowledge and behaviour.

The challenge for the future is to develop mechanisms whereby clinical behaviour may be coaxed in the direction of rationality, without jeopardising the high level of organisational commitment felt by most doctors (Freddi, 1989).

CHAPTER 7

What is to be Done?

Stephen Frankel and Robert West

The theme that has emerged in this book is that waiting lists occur in the National Health Service (NHS) in Britain not only through deficiencies in the system, but also through its design. In considering the general question of access to health care, the book has examined waiting lists not so much as an aberration of our health care system, which can be solved by 'initiatives', but as a consequence of the way that health care is ordered in Britain.

The interpretation that waiting lists are a straightforward expression of the inadequacy of resources, misses the point that waiting lists are the consequence of many individual decisions. Each may or may not be rational in its local context but in composite these decisions produce a pattern that is contrary to the stated aims of the NHS (Beveridge, 1942). Waiting lists are misunderstood if they are taken simply as evidence of the necessity for rationing of finite health care resources. Instead, they are better understood in terms of a discrepancy between the rationality of the service as a whole and the rationality of the many individual decisions which make up the whole. The importance of this analysis is that it suggests that waiting lists are unlikely to be reduced by policy changes designed to influence the level of overall rationing. Whatever resources become available, the current levels of unacceptable waiting are likely to be reduced only by policy changes directed at the more intimate decisions of patient management.

THE FUNCTIONS OF WAITING LISTS

Waiting lists are conventionally considered to be a problem, and discussion of waiting lists is customarily conducted with implicit acceptance of that premise. However the persistence of waiting lists suggests that they might usefully be viewed as a solution to other problems. Within the overall provision of health care lie a number of apparently contradictory objectives. Waiting lists may provide solutions to a number of these constituent objectives. The waiting list 'problem' cannot be 'solved' unless the solutions that waiting lists themselves offer are held to be genuinely unacceptable. Before looking for solutions it is necessary to be more explicit about these functions of the waiting list.

First, waiting lists blur the issue of health care rationing. All of those in need who demand treatment are nominally offered it, even if there is little serious intention of fulfilling the offer. It is ironic that demand for elective surgery has come to be regarded as unsatisfiable, for, as we consider later in this chapter, it would appear that this is an area of provision where reasonable levels of demand could realistically be met.

Second, waiting lists may serve to protect individual patients and practitioners from being forced to acknowledge either the triviality or the intractability of particular conditions. A significant proportion of patients on waiting lists, particularly outpatient waiting lists, are unlikely to benefit from surgery. Nevertheless the act of offering a consultant appointment may be preferable to denying the patient any prospect of relief.

Third, waiting lists can serve to maintain departmental and personal prestige and to demonstrate need for enhanced resources. The presence of long waiting lists is widely acknowledged as one of the most successful arguments for obtaining further resources. Waiting lists may also serve to feed private practice.

Fourth, waiting lists can be seen as a device for increasing efficiency in clinics, operating theatres and wards, by minimising staff idle time and maximising patient throughput or the patient/doctor ratio. Waiting lists allow elective surgery to compete with emergency surgery for the same beds. It is generally thought that an alternative system which separates the provision of elective and emergency surgery, would mean more empty beds and idle time for staff and so would be more expensive.

Finally the capitation fee system for remunerating general practitioners offers no incentive for managing more complex cases and so has encouraged general practitioners to refer to hospital some patients whose treatment they could reasonably have undertaken.

Hence waiting lists could appear to be in everyone's interest but that of the patient. Despite being possibly an over-simple summary, it will be appreciated that waiting for hospital treatment does serve many functions and is driven by powerful economic forces, as recognised, not only by Cullis in Chapter 2, but also by the other contributors to this volume. Accordingly the reader will appreciate that to change the waiting position in a significant way will require fundamental or radical changes in policy. In this chapter we will attempt to review both modifications of practice within the existing service which should contribute to an increase in throughput and a reduction in numbers waiting, and more radical reorganisations or redefinitions which, by attacking the problem at its roots, might achieve more than marginal change.

Since few problems are new problems, few solutions are likely to be new solutions. Doctors and others in the health services have been conscious for a long time of the chronic waiting problem and, as a consequence, many of the more concerned have suggested ways of reducing lists and easing the problem. In considering new moves and even radical solutions we should not belittle the many serious attempts which have been made in the past to alleviate the condition. We should consider whether some of the past suggestions have made apparently little dent on the overall situation because they were only partially or half-heartedly executed. It is possible that the same suggestions more thoroughly introduced or more completely adopted could produce more significant change on what the British public had come to accept as normal. It is also possible that a combination of past suggestions, introduced as a package and acting together on the problem, could have very different results from their past piecemeal introduction. Finally, it is possible that past suggestions were before their time and that if they were introduced now into a different economic/social welfare climate they would be more effective.

ADMINISTRATIVE RESPONSES

We will first consider the potential for administrative solutions, practical measures such as removing 'ghosts' from lists, identifying bottlenecks and increasing throughput. As the problem queue is relatively short in terms of total NHS throughput and the waiters are mostly waiting for relatively few surgical operations in terms of the variety of activities undertaken in the NHS, it might be thought that reducing waiting lists to acceptable proportions would not be too difficult.

It has been emphasised in previous chapters that patients are not referred to the NHS waiting lists but rather that general practitioners, with their independent contractor status substantially maintained through several NHS reorganisations, refer patients to their specialist colleagues, who still enjoy many of the privileges of independence of the pre-NHS voluntary honorary consultants, despite being salaried since 1948. It may appear from the outside that a hospital has a list of waiters and in turn so has the health authority and the NHS. However the waiting list is not so much an NHS list, a health authority list or a hospital list as an aggregate of individual surgeons' lists. No-one adds the numbers of people waiting for plumbers, painters or builders because there is no national service for plumbing, painting or building, but, if aggregated, these numbers could be as large as the numbers waiting for surgery. It is therefore, perhaps slightly incongruous that the 'service' takes the blame for the gross list.

The term administrator may still be more apt than the more forceful 'manager' for, despite the introduction of general management in the NHS (Griffiths, 1983), the unit general manager has had little effective jurisdiction over nurses and doctors. It is doctors particularly who have most influence on the flow of patients. Before the introduction of general management, it was manifestly obvious that hospitals, and indeed the whole health service, was not 'managed'. Major hospitals operated under a mixture of guidance from the Department of Health, hospital boards or health authorities, and various committees with a broad sense of co-operation and goodwill stemming from a belief in the beneficence underlying the whole health care industry. The administrator was a facilitator, but in no real sense managed the resources (human or material) of the hospital. In the conventional sense of the term the consultants (specialists) were, and perhaps still are, the managers, in that they had, and perhaps still have, most influence over the use of resources.

Prior to the introduction of general management it was often remarked that no industrial company would tolerate two score managing directors, each with his own set of objectives, often significantly at variance with the objectives of colleagues, yet sharing physical and personnel resources with them. Most new recruits to hospital administration, and most management consultants called in to examine some aspects of the waiting list problem, immediately recognise the organisational structure of the typical hospital as, at best, a delicately balanced co-operative depending heavily on mutual collaboration and goodwill and, at worst, a set of feuding factions with only the most general common purpose. Despite the impression that many potential patients have of the modern hospital, it remains a huge amalgam of very disparate entities.

It is with appreciation of the absence of an accountable management structure in the most powerful and influential profession in the hospital service that the NHS reorganisations have attempted to modify the organisational framework of the hospital services. However, the health service is huge, has inertia to match its size and has a long history of established working practices. Consequently the change in name from administrator to manager has made relatively little real change in many areas of the service. We will return to this issue, but meanwhile we consider the practical ways in which the hospital administrator or manager can tackle more problematic waiting lists.

Bottlenecks

The first administrative response that we will consider is the range of practical ways in which bottlenecks in the system can be identified and throughput increased. Competent hospital administrators will be aware of constraints in the system, mismatch between provision of resources at different points in the system, staff shortages or absences leading to underprovision in certain areas or to cancellations of outpatient clinics or theatre sessions. Yates (1987) has made many practical suggestions as to how the hospital administrator can achieve gains. Problems can often be attributed to mismatch of outpatient sessions to theatre time, or theatre time to ITU staffing or to bed numbers. More often than not the limiting constraint is well known to several of those who work in the chain, but who may have, or consider that they have, little direct influence over the constraint. The sensitive and able administrator or manager can obtain the relevant information from those who are more closely involved in the patient flow and can facilitate matters by appropriate redistribution of staff or resources.

Some appreciation of queuing theory is invaluable, even if queuing analysis is not formally undertaken. Probably the most important single feature of queuing theory which leads to a better understanding of NHS waiting lists is the appreciation that there are many sub-queues within the overall queue. This enables the administrator to identify more easily the bottlenecks or resource constraints which limit the overall flow

Reviews

Internal reviews are very important and often bring into the open information that has been available, but perhaps not generally acknowledged. Information is the universal key and it is because of the power of information that regular review or audit can contribute so significantly to the smoother and more efficient operation of complicated organisations, like the hospital service, which depend on much mutual cooperation and collaboration. Review or *ad hoc* study of a specific perceived problem is often initiated by some external stimulus: a Parliamentary question, a Department of Health initiative, a question by a health authority member or a new consultant appointment. While such review often brings to light something known but hitherto left unchallenged, the fact of the external stimulus to enquire and to act, shakes the *status quo* and the staff, who had previously accepted the problem as a fact of life. The 'Hawthorne effect' of a review may well be sufficient to motivate staff, encourage more collaborative activity and generally facilitate the flow of patients through the hospital.

External reviews, whether undertaken by health authority teams, by academics or by management consultants, can operate in much the same way as internal reviews. Like internal reviews, they are usually initiated by some external stimulus. They usually bring information to the forefront, encourage open discussion of the perceived problems, identify common features in the perceived problems and identify some constraint limiting the patient flow – constraints that are usually well known to at least some of the hospital staff. They may achieve some gain in patient throughput by advising some restructuring of responsibilities, redistribution or rescheduling of resources. It is arguable whether external review is more efficacious than internal review. Well conducted, external review probably is more able to encourage some protagonists with firmly entrenched beliefs and working practices to see the situation anew and to try new procedures. Badly or insensitively conducted, it is probably more likely to harden attitudes against the implied criticisms of outsiders who 'don't understand what we are up against' or 'what we are trying to achieve'.

The practical measures themselves hardly need enumerating, since they mostly involve reallocation of resources (beds, wards, theatre sessions, outpatient clinics) and staff (consultants, clinical assistants, junior doctors, nurses, clerical staff), rescheduling of sessions or clinics and revised allocation of backup services (diagnostic sessions, laboratory sessions, convalescent beds). These measures may be short term to clear a backlog, which may have accumulated over a relatively short period of ward closure, understaffing or strike, or they may be long term, when the perceived needs are deemed to have altered significantly and permanently over time.

Campaign or Blitz

Awareness of a waiting problem may lead to a campaign or blitz against waiting. Campaigns in the past have met with varying degrees of success, ranging from the steady reduction or even extinction of a list to no noticeable effect other than repeated discussion, and possibly report writing, over the importance of the issue. Many waiting lists have been the subject of concentrated attack with extra outpatient clinics, extra theatre sessions, Saturday or night operating sessions, borrowed staff, borrowed beds, or temporary extra consultant appointments. Even though a blitz may yield dramatic results and may reduce the waiting list quite quickly, it is not at all infrequent for the list to grow back with remarkable speed, fuelling the belief in the inevitability of waiting for treatment in the NHS. Whether a campaign or a blitz, the results are often much more permanent if introduced and undertaken by a new surgeon inheriting a list than if introduced and encouraged by administrators or managers. The clinician has greater influence over the list than does the administrator or manager, and there is much truth in the observation that the surgeon who believes that there *should* be no waiting over one month *has* no waiting over one month.

In the late 1980s waiting again became a political priority, and a major initiative was launched. The most concerted programme of management adjustments focussed on the 100 worst waiting lists in England (Inter-Authority Comparisons and Consultancy, 1990). The interventions were of three broad sorts. Waiting lists were properly validated, and 'ghosts' removed. Then additional operations were arranged through the better use of existing resources, or through additional resources where these offered identifiable increases in activity. Thirdly, operations were scheduled to the advantage of those whose waits had been longer. By these uncontroversial means the overall numbers waiting on these lists fell by 14% over a nine month period and, more significantly, the numbers of those waiting over 12 months fell by 26%. These findings indicate the value of the sorts of management initiatives that are available to all hospitals, and the unnecessary nature of a significant proportion of long waits. Where new resources were allocated, this was done on the basis of successful waiting lists reduction. The effectiveness of this initiative is strong evidence that waiting lists represent an artefact of the organisation of surgical care. The impact of this focussed initiative, which was funded at a level of some £13 million, is also in marked contrast to the parallel conventional investment in waiting list reduction, which demonstrated the usual lack of clear benefit from allocations from the Waiting List Fund of some £80 million (House of Commons Health Committee, 1991).

CHANGING STYLES OF PRACTICE

The measures that we refer to as administrative involve either doing more of the same, or doing the same in a more ordered manner. Further opportunities for rendering unnecessary long delays in the provision of elective surgery are offered by measures which involve greater adjustments in conventions concerning surgical practice. These involve practices whose efficacy and acceptability are not in serious doubt, but which for a variety of reasons many not have been given the prominence they may merit.

Short Stay and Day Surgery

The potential conflict between concerns with quality of care and quantity of throughput has already been raised. The case of day surgery for certain routine operations appears to be unusual in that the appropriate application of short stay surgery appears to satisfy both objectives. A number of studies have demonstrated that outcomes of day surgery for uncomplicated cases are comparable while costs are less (Russell *et al.*, 1977; Pineault *et al.*, 1985). There is little indication that short stays are less acceptable to patients. Despite this favourable picture and the approval of the Royal College of Surgeons of England (1985) for an expansion of day surgery, day surgery has not been widely adopted by British surgeons in the treatment of the main waiting list conditions (Henderson *et al.*, 1989). The Audit Commission (1990) reviewed this issue and concluded that, if day surgery were to be practised at uncontroversial levels for twenty common procedures, an additional 186 000 patients could be treated per annum within existing resources. An expansion of day surgery consistent with the stated professional view of its appropriateness, could lead to the treatment of some 300 000 additional patients per annum, equivalent to 34% of the current day-case and inpatient waiting list.

A number of barriers to the expansion of day surgery have been suggested (Audit Commission, 1990; Morgan and Beech, 1990). These include a lack of specialist facilities or the inefficient use of those which do exist, as well as clinicians' preference for conventional admission and lack of incentive to change. Further disincentives to reduce lengths of stay and introduce more day surgery, are being removed by the new funding arrangements under the NHS and Community Care Act (1990). Until now fixed budgets have had a restraining effect upon increases in throughput. The new funding arrangements offer clear incentives for efficiency. It is likely that this innovation will have effects analogous to those in the United States, where financial incentives for shorter lengths of stay led to rapid changes in hospital and surgical practice (Morgan and Beech 1990).

Booking Procedures

It is asserted that some classes of patients in the USA may actually wait longer than patients in the UK (Light, 1990). However, waiting is organised differently in the USA: because patients have definite appointments, they do not see themselves as waiting. This indicates the importance of the uncertainty of waiting, as distinct from the actual time spent waiting.

The current arrangements for patient admission for elective surgery may seem archaic and out of step with the public's experience of other services. In a consumer-orientated National Health Service it would clearly be preferable to offer most patients at the time of the outpatient assessment, a mutually agreeable date for admission. This solution, where patients are either given a date for admission or not accepted as the responsibility of the hospital, would effectively abolish waiting lists. Since the waiting list may be regarded as a somewhat arbitrary administrative device, representing only one amongst many routes for gaining access to inpatient care (Sykes, 1986), an administrative artefact may be amenable to administrative decree. Booking all patients instead of adding them to waiting lists would provide a deceptively simple means for abolishing waiting lists.

It is perhaps a striking feature of the medical literature that those aspects of health care delivery which may be of major interest to patients may not be the subject of serious scrutiny. The literature on booking systems is particularly meagre. Patients themselves find that it is the lack of a booking system that is remarkable: when one booking system was introduced, not one out of several thousand patients remarked upon it (Southam and Talbot, 1980). A number of planned or booked admissions systems have been operated by individual hospitals (Duthie, 1973; Devlin, 1980; DHSS, 1981). Administration of booking systems depends upon a relatively predictable length of stay. An interesting observation was that the proportion of emergency admissions has been found to fall (Devlin, 1980; Southam and Talbot, 1980), suggesting that a significant proportion of emergency admissions can be avoided by the use of a coherent admissions policy. Failed admissions become less common with booking systems (Southam and Talbot, 1980; Houghton and Brodribb, 1989). Booking systems may also reduce the temptation to defer some patients' admissions indefinitely because their conditions are 'routine' or 'uninteresting' (Cox, 1977).

In the normal NHS system, with limited bed provision and theatre time, patients requiring elective procedures must in general compete with those admitted as emergencies (Frankel *et al.*, 1991). The demands for emergency admission fluctuate, with a correspondingly inverse effect upon the availability of beds and theatre time for elective surgery. The putative advantage of these arrangements is an efficient use of resources, but this efficiency if paid for by the patient in terms of uncertainty and cancelled admissions (Frankel *et al.*, 1989). The patient has no knowledge of the likely date of the operation and therefore can make no plans for hospitalisation. Such uncertainties in the timing of the operation are costs for the patient and may outweigh the costs of lost throughput, but anyway they are inconsistent with a consumer-orientated health service.

The uncertainty of generic waiting lists could be replaced by booking procedures as used in certain areas of health care, such as dentistry, but such systems would inevitably break down if bookings were often or regularly cancelled to make way for emergencies. The scope for the efficient use of beds through what would amount to double booking is therefore diminished. The cost to the service of moving from waiting list systems to booked admissions systems, whilst continuing to treat the same number of patients, would be little more than the relatively modest fixed cost of the required number of additional beds. Some of the economic disbenefit of a pure booking system could be offset by a combination of booked admissions with a pool of patients, willing to be admitted at short notice. It is likely that this may in fact be the most efficient system of all. This system could reduce costs of uncertainty to the majority of patients, as with the booked admissions system, but could minimise the inefficiency of a reduced throughput. The introduction and acceptance of a booking system, particularly if it were intended to embrace the bulk of elective surgery, would bring into unequivocal relief the extent that the NHS is capable of responding to demand, both in terms of numbers of cases and the conditions that affect them. The use of a booking system for most routine surgery would remove the veil over unsatisfiable demand which is offered by the amorphous waiting lists.

Private Practice

One very important feature of the organisation of specialist medicine in the NHS has been the contract of employment of consultants. Specialists inherited from pre-NHS days an expectation to work both for the service and, if they so wished, privately. Although levels of payment changed radically at the formation of the NHS, when honorary and unpaid consultants began to receive proper salaries, the freedom to practice privately continued. Since most consultants are now full time, or very nearly full time, in theory they work in private practice in evenings and at weekends, as any other employee might have a second part-time job or a paying hobby.

However, because of requirements to be on call to provide cover some nights and some weekends, it is easier for consultants to be 'out of the office' during office hours than it is for almost any other employee. It is possible for consultants to spend much of the normal working week in private facilities, with NHS work being undertaken by doctors in training grades, often without open complaint, because they are dependent on personal references to obtain, in their turn, their own consultant appointments. Thus consultants or specialists within the hospital service may legitimately 'moonlight' during the working week.

In this context a long waiting list may by seen to be very desirable; it limits the amount of work that has to be done in the hospital and at the same time it encourages patients to consider the price of private consultation and treatment. To overcome this long established effect, there seems to be no real alternative to some radical revision of the consultant contract. Why should not consultants be obliged to work their agreed sessions during office hours and also, as part of their job description or terms of employment, to accept a rota for night/weekend cover, just as do registrars and general practitioners? That would still allow the 'workaholics' to engage in private practice in the evenings, in time when they could be enjoying their family or their recreations. A less radical alternative would be an element of piecework in the consultant's salary, but the dangers here are obvious. Piecework payment incentives would be likely to encourage dermatology (and ten minute consultations) at the expense of psychiatry (and ten year cases) and, secondly, within a specialty, would encourage cases rather than cures. The free market economist could recommend mechanisms to price each specialty and each item of service, but any such mechanism raises the real cost of the service, since it introduces further stages of middle management and data collection.

THE MANAGEMENT OF DEMAND

An important feature of waiting lists is that they permit a blurring of the National Health Service's capacity for or commitment to certain sorts of treatment. Waiting lists veil the discrepancies which exist between what is offered and what can be done. To be on a waiting list is to be betwixt and between; to be accepted as a suitable case for treatment, even if the prospect of that treatment being delivered may be distant or absent. There are various implications of confronting this fiction. The problem presented to patients and practitioners of making explicit the improbability of any benefit from the referral has already been mentioned. We consider next the relationship between demand and provision of services, for any fundamental response to the waiting list problem must confront the management of demand.

Levels of Demand

The view that demand is infinite is rarely made explicit (Frankel, 1991b). The view is nevertheless common and is implicit in the criticism of the supposed naivety of the founders of the NHS for expecting demand to fall as the backlog of morbidity was cleared. The frequently used metaphor of the 'iceberg' of morbidity supports the view that unmet need for health care activity is unchanging: if infinite the pool of untreated illness would remain constant, whatever level of intervention is contemplated.

This relatively impressionistic view of the overwhelming nature of demand appears to concur with the simple view of health economics which has gained wide currency in debates of health policy. The health economists' pursuit of more rational grounds for the allocation of finite resources between competing ends may appear to indicate the necessity of rationing in all areas of health care provision. However, it is important to remember that the view that demand in general may exceed supply does not necessarily imply that particular forms of demand cannot be satisfied. The large variations in levels of surgical provision point to the difficulties in determining the appropriate level for particular procedures (Bunker, 1970; Wennberg *et al.*, 1987).

Since waiting lists are taken as an indicator of demand, the intractability of waiting lists sustains the conventional view of the infinity of demand. However, it is important to point out the deficiencies of focussing almost exclusively upon what is *not* performed by the health care system in attempting to assess the feasibility of satisfying demand. If instead we focus upon what *is* done, the picture may appear rather different. It has already been observed that the level of research into the waiting list conditions is strikingly meagre, particularly when it is the seeming failure to satisfy demand for these conditions that has provided the main impetus for a major reorganisation of the NHS. Population studies which would be relevant to an informed debate concerning potential demand for treatment for the waiting list conditions are particularly notable for their absence (Frankel, 1991a).

To put unmet demand into context, we might take the example of the total hip replacement (THR), a key waiting list condition of certain cost-effectiveness, where demand appears difficult to satisfy. The principal population-based assessment of need for this operation found that some 1.2% of those over 65 years of age were regarded as requiring and able to tolerate THR, and includes those subjects whose hips had already been replaced (Wilcock 1979). That study may now be somewhat dated, because threshold levels for THR have been revised. Nevertheless it is striking that estimates of current prevalences of those with replaced hips greatly exceed Wilcock's prevalences of those satisfying his criteria of need. For example it appears that some 3% of 65–74 year old females have received hip replacements (Frankel *et al.* 1990). In the older age groups estimated rates for completed THRs rise towards 6%. Similarly, high levels of operative activity in the other waiting list conditions may lead to comparably high current prevalences of treated cases. Clearly the relevant disease frequency to measure is incidence (the number of new cases in the population per unit time). The ideal of achieving rates of operative activity that approximate to levels of incident disease may be a realistic objective.

One possible explanation of the wide variations in population-based rates of use of medical and surgical procedures as well as the apparent difficulty in satisfying demand is that a proportion of interventions may be inappropriate (Chassin *et al.*, 1987a; Kahn *et al.*, 1988). The policy implication of research into appropriateness and variation is that providers can be constrained to conform to clinical guidelines through reimbursement arrangements (Shortell and McNerney, 1990), though there are clear disincentives for these policies being implemented (Evans, 1990). An interest in defining the indications for treatment is given added momentum in the USA by a wish to control the escalating costs of health care; defined criteria of appropriateness offer a mechanism for limiting entitlement for reimbursement. It is paradoxical that, within the centrally funded British system, clinicians have resisted attempts to curtail idiosyncratic practice through adherence to guidelines more successfully than have their nominally more entrepreneurial counterparts in the USA. While the widespread adherence to guidelines for treatment thresholds is a distant prospect in Britain, attempts are being made to introduce the concept of guidelines with minimal controversy and confrontation through the mechanism of clinical audit.

Audit and practice guidelines

Clinical audit has different meanings for different people, but the activity is now becoming much more widely accepted as a desirable and necessary feature of good clinical care. Most audits are likely to involve review of working practices and setting of guidelines or targets, before monitoring practices to see that the guidelines are followed and the targets achieved. Clinician-led audit, aiming for the most effective and up-to-date therapy, and management-led audit, seeking efficiency and higher patient throughput as prime objectives, may well achieve very similar ends. However, it should be appreciated that one of the grounds for clinicians' suspicions of management-led audit is that the pursuit of the throughput statistic will affect quality of care. Managers should certainly appreciate, or be regularly reminded, that the vast majority of statistics which are available (because they are the more easily measurable) are statistics only of quantity and not of quality (West, 1987). Good sensitive management will blend the primary concern of the clinician for individual patients and the primary concern of the health care planner for populations to achieve both quality for the individual patient and quantity of patients.

It is important to point out the limited impact of guidelines even in uncontroversial areas of practice. There is an uncertain relationship between statements of supposedly ideal practice and their adoption by practitioners (Hill *et al.*, 1988, Wortman *et al.*, 1988, Lomas *et al.* 1989) , so that even very simple guidelines, such as those concerning the use of diagnostic tests, have been shown to have a limited impact upon clinical practice (Hall *et al.* 1988). It would therefore be naive to expect too much from the audit/guideline cycle in redirecting the thrust of NHS activity.

Other means of reinforcing the acceptance of practice guidelines may be more effective, such as the focus upon opinion leaders rather than the conventional process of feedback to the generality of practitioners (Lomas *et al.*, 1989).

While clinical audit can easily be described and clinical guidelines can easily be laid down in theory for the 'average patient', when it comes to implementation, we are soon confronted with the problem of the common 'non average' patient. In the context of reducing waiting lists, the threshold of sickness, illness or disability is of considerable interest. Although we may suspect that the system of referral, admission and treatment is not operating in a perfectly rational and fair way, we can infer that patients accorded low priority on long lists are left there because they are not perceived to be as sick, ill, disabled or in need of treatment as others; in other words, that they are only slightly sick. The rational response would be to define the threshold of disability at which a disorder is classified as a disease or as a disease deserving of treatment by the state. Although easy and logical in principle, the processes of defining a referral threshold, and then implementing it, are not simple in practice, as can be illustrated by a study of orthopaedic waiting.

A long list may comprise nearly one third of patients who are no longer seeking treatment for a variety of reasons, one third returning with old problems that have not resolved following previous specialist treatment, as well as the one third who are likely to benefit from specialist treatment (West and McKibbin, 1982). The first group, those no longer seeking treatment, has been more widely described in the past. They may have recovered spontaneously, may have sought treatment elsewhere, may have learned to live with the disability or pain, may have moved away, or died. Because as many as one third of patients on a long list no longer seek treatment, the process of waiting has been described as beneficial. Practitioners are saved some unnecessary work and patients are saved some unnecessary medication or surgical intervention. Some guidelines relating to minor conditions may be accepted implicitly by many referring general practitioners. However, until guidelines are stated explicitly, and accepted, there will continue to be variation in the referral threshold at this mild end of the need scale, because patients and general practitioners acting for patients will have varying perceptions of the disability, its natural prognosis and of what can be offered by the specialist.

There is much less discussion in the literature of the second group of patients on long waiting lists: those with chronic intractable problems that are still not resolved following previous specialist investigation who are seeking to try the system again. Waiting lists offer a means for avoiding any explicit statement that a patient's condition is unlikely to be remediable. Guidelines would seem rational, to advise the referring general practitioners which conditions are not amenable to surgical intervention.

Here again we would not expect guidelines to eliminate all uncertainty or self-referral, since the eternal optimism of some will mean that they will continue to seek multiple revisions or reoperations. However, guidelines on which conditions are less suitable for intervention after full specialist assessment, coupled with improved communication between specialists and general practitioners, both in long term policy and over individual patients, should make it possible to reduce significantly the numbers of 'no-hopers' who appear to be dumped on to waiting lists.

From the perspective of either the general practitioner service or the specialist hospital service, there is little incentive to develop or implement guidelines in that both can use the waiting list to keep patients out of the surgery or clinic. However, from the point of view of an integrated service for a population, both would probably accept that it is less logical and, perhaps inhumane to park these patients on the list or allow them to wait for long periods without explaining adequately that the wait for them is all but pointless. An integrated service should be better able to draw general practitioners and specialists together to collaborate more closely towards the communal goal than the previous separated services, and sensitive management of an integrated service should facilitate this collaboration more effectively than the administrators of the past in the separated services.

The implementation of guidelines may go further than management and may involve a fundamental review of NHS policy. Here guidelines become relevant for the third group of patients on waiting lists: those who may reasonably expect to benefit from specialist treatment. The question then becomes: is it possible to define what is legitimate activity for the NHS and can that be defined in terms of guidelines describing who and what to treat?

At the limit we probably all accept that there are conditions which are not recognised as diseases and, as a consequence, which do not deserve to be treated by the NHS. Examples might include certain minor sports injuries, where the hurt sportsperson would probably think first of visiting a physiotherapist rather than a general practitioner. While for some active sportspeople the preference for physiotherapy over a general practitioner consultation may be judged in terms of the expected benefits of treatment, many would see such a self-imposed condition as being outside the remit of the NHS. This seed has survived from pre-NHS days. The cultivator of an alternative service for certain definable mild or temporary conditions needs only to nurture that seed. There may be argument about the inequity, divisiveness and practical difficulty of defining those conditions which are and are not eligible for free treatment by the NHS and argument might be heated. Yet such argument is an essential preliminary to the task of making explicit the limits to potential provision, rather than concealing such limits within waiting lists.

PURCHASERS, PROVIDERS AND THE MANAGEMENT OF WAITING

For many decades the measures that were introduced to tackle waiting lists were somewhat peripheral to the fundamental origins of the waiting list. However, the NHS review which began in January 1988, as a response to widely publicised individual waiting problems, is addressed primarily at refashioning those aspects of the NHS culture that support waiting lists. The reforms can therefore be best understood as the definitive waiting list initiative. The current health service reforms represent, at one level, an attempt to give those who are held accountable for waiting lists some greater influence over them. Until now health authorities have been held responsible for waiting lists, but have possessed only the most tenuous power to effect their reduction. Waiting lists were more influenced by specialists, who were under conflicting pressures. The wish to deliver an impeccable service to the patients referred was countered by the value of a waiting list in securing new funding and a reputation for being sought after. A long waiting list brought no particular sanctions for the individual best placed to deal with it; indeed there were some perverse incentives supporting the accumulation of waiting patients.

The reorganisation of the NHS consequent upon the National Health Service and Community Care Act (1990) represents a more fundamental reform than any which has been attempted since the inception of the Service. The key innovation of the Act is the separation of the functions of purchasing and providing services. Health authorities as purchasers are now expected to specify the volume and quality of the services they deem desirable for their resident populations. Hospitals, and the doctors who work in the hospitals, are to become the providers. This is a fundamental departure from existing practice. Purchasing authorities will be in a position to make explicit the nature of the clinical activity they regard as desirable, which will lead to a radical shift in the nature of clinical freedom. The continuing debate about clinical freedom, which is at the heart of this proposal, appears to have reached a new phase. Wide appreciation amongst the medical profession of the need to be concerned by the resource implications of their decisions has coincided with wide acceptance of the value of routine audit of their work. The debate between politicians and doctors has centred upon management or control of these activities, rather than on whether they should be conducted at all.

These reforms are likely to alter the ways in which the waiting list has blurred the imbalance between demand and provision. Where purchase and provision of services are truly separated, the requirements for therapeutic and surgical activity are set by the purchasing authority. Where specified levels of surgery do not satisfy demand, then the purchasing authority is responsible, not the providing authority or surgeon. If the purchasing authority has made its estimate of need correctly, patients satisfying prior agreed disability thresholds and admission criteria will be admitted. If, however, the demand or referral exceeds the purchasing authorities' estimates, or if there continues to be ambiguity over the degree of disability that warrants treatment, the patient may be referred back to await next year's renegotiated quota. The patients may still be waiting but waiting at a different 'door'.

Recent moves from administration to management and the present health service reorganisation are clearly designed to reduce the traditional independence and power of clinicians. Previous attempts to render these key NHS workers more managerially accountable have resulted in relatively little change. How far current developments will be effective in bringing clinicians to work to an employing manager's design remains to be seen.

CONCLUSION

The argument in this book has several strands. The broadest view which emerges from the detailed examinations of waiting concerns the question of rationing finite health care resources. There is no question that rationing is inherent in the resourcing of health care provision. Demand for health care may outstrip the resources made available. However, within this global pattern of scarcity, the finer analysis presented here suggests that long waiting times for some people and for some operations are not the consequence of any global mismatch between supply and demand but an expression of the implicit priorities within health care provision, which are themselves the product of a range of organisational factors and professional preferences.

Rationing certainly exists in the National Health Service, as it does in any health care system. However the current system of rationing in Britain appears highly irrational in that the very conditions where comparatively cheap interventions are likely to lead to considerable health benefits are those selected for relative neglect. It is ironic that those very conditions, where a rational application of current resources could reasonably be expected to satisfy demand, are held up as evidence for the need for rationing.

Bibliography

Abel-Smith, B. (1964). *The Hospitals, 1800–1948: a Study in Social Administration in England and Wales*. Heinemann, London

Adler, M. W., Waller, J. J, Creese, A. and Thorne, S. C. (1978). Randomised controlled trial of early discharge for inguinal hernia and varicose veins. *Journal of Epidemiology and Community Health*, **32**, 136–42

Aldis, A. S. (1984). *Cardiff Royal Infirmary 1883–1983*. University of Wales Press, Cardiff

Anderson, P., Meara, J., Brodhurst, S., Attwood, S., Timbrell, M. and Gatherer, A. (1988). Use of hospital beds: a cohort study of admissions to a provincial teaching hospital. *British Medical Journal*, **297**, 910–12

Anderson, T. F., Mooney, G. (1990). *The Challenges of Medical Practice Variations*. London: Macmillan

Anonymous. (1853a). Abuse of hospitals and dispensaries, a monster evil of the day. *British Medical Journal*, **1**, 76–7

Anonymous. (1853b). The growing abuses of hospitals and dispensaries. *British Medical Journal*, **1**, 201

Anonymous. (1853c). Hospital abuse: a glance at Nottingham, Bath and Bolton. *British Medical Journal*, **1**, 315–16

Anonymous. (1853d). Hospital abuses, advice gratis and medical benevolence. *British Medical Journal*, **2**, 429

Anonymous. (1875). Provident institutions and hospitals. I – Outpatient departments. *British Medical Journal*, 27 March 1875, 416–17

Anonymous. (1878). Consultants' professional etiquette. *British Medical Journal*, **26**, 666

Anonymous. (1884). Medical etiquette. *British Medical Journal*, **1**, 744, 838, 881–2, 1184–5

Anonymous. (1886). Consultants and general practitioners. *British Medical Journal*, **2**, 1114–15

Anonymous. (1913). The reform of the hospital out-patient department. *British Medical Journal*, **1**, 403–4

Anonymous. (1931). *Hospital*, Volume 27, January

Anonymous. (1946). Consultants and specialists and the Bill. *British Medical Journal*, **1** (Suppl.), 151

Anonymous. (1972). An answer to the surgical waiting-list. *Lancet*, **ii**, 23–4

Anonymous. (1976a). To come again, 3 months. *Lancet*, **i**, 1168–9

Anonymous. (1976b). Outpatient follow-up. *Journal of the Royal College of General Practitioners*, **26**, 762–3

Anonymous. (1985). Wide variation in hospital waiting times and lists. *British Medical Journal*, **290**, 577–8

Anonymous. (1987a). Government plans for reduction of NHS waiting lists. *Lancet*, **i**, 520

Anonymous. (1987b). Down with waiting lists and times. *Lancet*, **i**, 784–5
Anonymous. (1988a) Cholecystectomy: the dissatified customer. *Lancet*, **i**, 339
Anonymous. (1988b). Measuring need for health care. *Lancet*, **i**, 29–30
Anonymous. (1989a). TU or not TU. *Lancet*, **i**, 1361–2
Anonymous. (1989b). Investigation of failed low back pain. *Lancet*, **i**, 939–40
Ashby, J., Buxton, M. and Gravelle, H. (1990). Will a breast screening programme change the workload and referral practice of general practitioners? *Journal of Epidemiology and Community Health*, **44**, 36–8
Ashmore, M., Mulkay, M. and Pinch, T. (1989). *Health and Efficiency: a Sociology of Health Economics*. Open University Press, Milton Keynes
Audit Commission (1990). *A Short Cut to Better Services: Day Surgery in England and Wales*. London: HMSO
Backett, E. M., Summer, G., Kilpatrick, J. and Dingwall-Fordyce, I. (1966). Hospitals in the north-east Scotland region. In Mclachlan, G. (Ed.), *Problems and Progress in Medical Care*. Nuffield Provincial Hospitals Trust, London/Oxford University Press
Balint, M. (1957). *The Doctor, His Patient and the Illness*. New York: Pitman Medical
Banks, M. H., Beresford, S. A. A., Morrell, D. C., Waller, J. J. and Watkins, C. J. (1975). Factors influencing demand for primary medical care in women aged 20–44 years: a preliminary report. *International Journal of Epidemiology*, **4**, 189–95
Barber, J. H. (1971). Computer assisted recording in general practice. *Journal of the Royal College of General Practitioners*, **21**, 726–36
Barr, A., McNeilly, R. H. and Rogers, S. (1982). Use of operating theatres. *British Medical Journal*, **285**, 1059–61
Bayliss, R. I. S. (1988). The National Health Service versus private and complementary medicine. *British Medical Journal*, **296**, 1457–9
Becker, G. S. (1965). A theory of the allocation of time. *Economic Journal*, **75** (299), 493–517
Bendixen, H. H. (1977). The cost of intensive care. In Bunker, J. P., Barnes, B. A. and Mosteller, F. (Eds.), *Costs, Risks and Benefits of Surgery*. Oxford University Press, New York
Benjamin, B. (1965). Hospital Activity Analysis: an information feedback for the consultant. *Hospital*, **61** (5), 221–8
Berg, R. L. (1973). Weighted life expectancy as health status index. *Health Services Research*, **8**, 153
Bergner, M., Bobbit, R. A., Kressel, A., Pollard, W. E., Gilson, B. S. and Morris, J. R. (1976). The Sickness Impact Profile. *International Journal of Health Services*, **6**, 393–415
Best, J. (1987). The length of a piece of string. *Medical Journal of Australia*, **147** (10), 513–14
Beveridge, W. H. (1942). *Social Insurance and Allied Services: Report*. His Majesty's Stationery Office, London
Birmingham Research Unit of the Royal College of General Practitioners. (1978). Practice activity analysis. 5. Referrals to specialists. *Journal of the Royal College of General Practitioners*, **28**, 251–2
Bishop, C. C. R. and Jarrett, P. E. M. (1986). Outpatient varicose vein surgery

under local anaesthesia. *British Journal of Surgery*, **73**, 821–2

Bloom, B. S. and Fendrick, A. M. (1987). Waiting for care: Queuing for resource allocation. *Medical Care*, **25**, 131–9

Bombardier, C., Ware, J., Russell, I. J., Larson, M., Chalmers, A. and Read J. L. (1986). Auranofin therapy and quality of life in patients with rheumatoid arthritis: results. *American Journal of Medicine*, **81** (4), 565–78

Bosanquet N, Fordham R, Outpatient services – a case for treatment. *Health Services Journal*, 14 May 1987: 550–1

Bourne, S. (1976). Second opinion: a study of medical referrals in a seminar for GPs at the Tavistock Clinic, London. *Journal of the Royal College of General Practitioners*, 26 (168), 487–95

Bradlaw, M. J. (1938). L. C. C. hospital out-patient departments. *British Medical Journal*, **2** (Suppl.), 157

British Medical Association. (1931). Report of Council on the problem of the out-patient. *British Medical Journal*, **2** (Suppl.), 53–5

Brook, R. H. (1979). Overview of adult health status measures. *Medical Care*, **17** (7, Suppl.), 1–131

Brook, R. H., Kosecoff, J. B., Park, R. E., Chassin, M. R., Winslow, C. M. and Hampton, J. R. (1988). Diagnosis and treatment of coronary disease: comparison of doctors' attitudes in the USA and the UK. *Lancet*, **i**, 750–3

Broome, J. (1987). Good, fairness and QALYs. In Bell, M. and Medus, S. (Eds.). *The Proceedings of the Royal Institute of Philosophy Conference on Philosophy and Medical Welfare*. Cambridge University Press, Cambridge

Brown, E. R. *et al.* (1987). *Californians without Health Insurance: A Report*. California Legislature

Browne, K. W. Freeling, P. (1976). *The doctor-patient relationship*. New York: Churchill Livingstone

Buchanan, J. M. (1965). *The Inconsistencies of the NHS*. Occasional Paper No. 7. Institute of Economic Affairs, London

Bulpitt, C. J., Daymond, M. J. and Dollery, C. T. (1982). Community care compared with hospital outpatient care for hypertensive patients. *British Medical Journal*, **284**, 554–6

Bunker, J. P. (1970). Surgical manpower: a comparison of operations and surgeons in the United States and England and Wales. *New England Journal of Medicine*, **282**, 135–44

Buttery, R. B. and Snaith, A. H. (1979). Waiting for surgery. *British Medical Journal*, **2**, 403–4

Buttery, R. B. and Snaith, A. H. (1980). Surgical provision, waiting times and waiting lists. *Health Trends*, **12**, 57–61

Buxton, M. J., Acheson, R., Caine, N., Gibson, S. and O'Brien, B. J. (1985). *Costs and Benefit of Heart Transplant Programmes*. DHSS Research Report No. 12. Her Majesty's Stationery Office, London

Carr-Hill, R. A. (1989). Assumptions of the QALY procedure. *Social Science and Medicine*, **29** (3), 469–77

Chamberlain, J. (1966). Two non-teaching hospitals in south-east England. In McLachlan, G. (Ed.), *Problems and Progress in Medical Care*. Nuffield Provincial Hospitals Trust, London/Oxford University Press

Chant, A. D. B., Jones, H. O. and Weddell, J. M. (1972). Varicose veins: a comparison of surgery and injection/compression sclerotherapy. *Lancet*, **ii**, 1188–91

Chassin, R., Brook, R. H., Park, R. E., Keesey, J., Fink, A., Kosecoff, J., Kahn, K., Merrick, N. and Solomon, D. H. (1986). Variations in the use of medical and surgical services by the medicare population. *New England Journal of Medicine*, **314**, 285–90

Chassin, M. R. *et al.* (1987a). Does inappropriate use explain geographic variations in the use of health care services? *Journal of the American Medical Association*, **258**, 2533–7

Chassin, M. R. *et al.* (1987b). How coronary angiography is used. *Journal of the American Medical Association*, **258**, 2543–7

Clare, A. (1989). National variations in medical practice. *British Medical Journal*, **298**, 1334

Cochrane, A. (1972). *Effectiveness and Efficiency*. Nuffield Provincial Hospitals Trust, London

Cochrane, J. P., Williams, J. F., Faber, R. G. and Slack, W. W. (1980). Value of out-patient follow-up after curative surgery for carcinoma of the large bowel. *British Medical Journal*, **280**, 593–5

Coggan, D. and Goldacre, M. J. (1976). Outpatient follow-up after appendectomy. *Lancet*, **i**, 1346–7

Coid, J. and Crome, P. (1986). Bed blocking in Bromley. *British Medical Journal*, **292**, 1253–6

College of Health. (1987). *Guide to Hospital Waiting Lists*. College of Health, London

Commission on the Provision of Surgical Services. (1986). *General Surgical Manpower within the United Kingdom*. Royal College of Surgeons of England, London

Cooke, M. and Ronalds, C. (1985). Women doctors in urban general practice: the patients. *British Medical Journal*, **290**, 753–5

Cooper, M. H. (1975). *Rationing Health Care*. Croom Helm, London

Cottrell, K. M. (1980). Waiting lists: some problems of definition and a relative measure of waiting time. *Hospital and Health Services Review*, **76**, 265–9

Coulter, A. and McPherson, K. (1986). The hysterectomy debate. *Quarterly Journal of Social Affairs*, **2**, 379–96

Coulter, A. and McPherson, K. (1987). Waiting times and duration of hospital stay for common surgical operations: trends over time. *Community Medicine*, **9**, 247–53

Coulter, A., Noone, A. and Goldacre, M. (1989). General practitioners' referrals to specialist outpatient clinics. I. Why general practitioners refer to specialist outpatients clinics. *British Medical Journal*, **299**, 304–8

Cox A. G., Admissions by the Book (1977) *The Lancet*, **i**, 301–2

Cox, D. R. and Smith, W. L. (1961). *Queues*. Chapman and Hall, London

Crombie, D. L. (1984). *Social Class and Health Status – Inequality or Difference*. Occasional paper No. 25. Royal College of General Practitioners, London

Cross, D. and Harris, C. (1974). *Fundamentals of Queuing Theory*. Wiley, New York

Cullis, J. G. and Jones P. R. (1983). Inpatient waiting: a discussion and policy proposal. *British Medical Journal*, **287**, 1483–6

Cullis, J. G. and Jones, P. R. (1985). NHS waiting lists: a discussion of competing explanations and a policy proposal. *Journal of Health Economics*, **4** (2), 119–35

Cullis, J. G. and Jones, P. R. (1986). Rationing by waiting lists: an implication. *American Economic Review*, **74** (1), 250–6

Culyer, A. J. and Cullis, J. G. (1976). Some economics of hospital waiting lists. *Journal of Social Policy*, **5** (3), 239–64

Culyer, A. J. (1983). Public or private health services?: a sceptic's view. *Journal of Policy Analysis and Management*, **2** (3), 386–402

Cummins, R. O., Jarman, B. and White, P. M. (1981). Do general practitioners have different 'referral thresholds'? *British Medical Journal*, **282**, 1037–9

Cybulska, J. P. and Rucinski, J. (1989). Communication between doctors. *British Journal of Hospital Medicine*, **41** (3), 266–8

Dalziel, M. and Kerr, R. (1987). Drums begin to beat in the waiting list jungle. *British Medical Journal*, **294**, 723–4

Davidge, M., Harley, M., Vickerstaff, L. and Yates, J. (1987). The anatomy of large inpatient waiting lists. *Lancet*, **i**, 794–6

de Alarcon, R. and Hodson, J. M. (1964). Value of the general practitioners' letter. A further study in medical communication. *British Medical Journal*, **2**, 435–8

Dean, M. (1991). Is your treatment economic, effective, efficient? *Lancet*, **337**, 480–1

Deitch, R. (1981a). The mystery of waiting lists and waiting times. *Lancet*, **ii**, 1122

Deitch, R. (1981b). How secure are figures for waiting NHS patients? *Lancet*, **ii**, 1179–80

Deitch, R. (1984). Broken NHS appointments: millions wasted? *Lancet*, **i**, 1419

Deitch, R. (1985). How much does it cost to cut NHS waiting lists by calling in the private sector? *Lancet*, **i**, 354

Department of Health and Social Security. *Orthopaedic Services: Waiting time for out-patient appointments and in-patient treatment*. Report of a Working Party to the Secretary of State for Social Services, 1981

Department of Health and Social Security. (1975). Reduction of Waiting Times for In-patient Admission: Management Arrangements. *HSC(IS)* **181**. DHSS, London

Department of Health. (1989). *Health and Personal Social Services Statistics for England*. Her Majesty's Stationery Office, London

Devlin H. B. Programmed elective surgery in Waiting for Hospital Treatment (1980). *Harrogate Seminar Reports*: 18–25. DHSS: London

Domenighetti, G., Luraschi, P., Casabianca, A., Gutzwiller, F., Spinelli, A., Pedrinis, E. and Repetto, F. (1988). Effect of information campaign by the mass media on hysterectomy rates. *Lancet*, **ii**, 1470–3

Don, B., Lee, A. and Goldacre, M. J. (1987). Waiting list statistics. III. Comparison of two measures of waiting times. *British Medical Journal*, **295**, 1247–8

Donaldson, L. J., Maratos, J. I. and Richardson, R. A. (1984). Review of an orthopaedic in-patient waiting list. *Health Trends*, **16**, 14–15

Dowie, R. (1983). *General Practitioners and Consultants: a Study of Outpatient Referrals*. King Edward's Hospital Fund for London

Drummond, M., (1991). Output measurement for resource allocation decisions, in McGuire, A., Fenn, P., and Mayhew, K. (Eds), *Providing*

Healthcare: the economics of alternative systems of finance and delivery. Oxford University Press, Oxford.

Duncan, M., Beale, K., Parry, J. and Miller, R. A. (1988). Outpatients: can we save time and reduce waiting lists? *British Medical Journal*, **296**, 247–8

Dunnell, K. and Cartwright, A. (1972). *Medicine-takers, Prescribers and Hoarders.* Routledge and Kegan Paul, London

Duthie R. B., Mullins J. L., Pace A. J. (1973). *The formation of an Admission Unit in a Specialist Hospital. Health Trends* 5: 4–7

Duthie, R. B. [Chairman.] (1981). *Orthopaedic Services: Waiting Times for Outpatient Apppointments and In-patient Treatment.* Her Majesty's Stationery Office, London

Eastaugh, S. R. (1980). Organisational determinants of surgical lengths of stay. *Inquiry*, **17**, 85–96

Eddy, D. M. (1984). Variations in physician practice: the role of uncertainty.*Health Affairs*, **3**, 74–89

Emmanuel, J. and Walter, N. (1989). Referrals from general practice to hospital outpatient departments: a strategy for improvement. *British Medical Journal*, **299**, 722–4

Evans, E. O. and McBride, K. (1968). Hospital usage by a group practice. *Journal of the Royal College of General Practitioners*, **16**, 294–306

Evans, R. G. (1990). The dog in the night-time: medical practice variations and health policy. In Andersen, T. F. and Mooney, G. (Eds.), *The Challenges of Medical Practice Variations.* Macmillan, London

Fair, J. F. (1989). Hospital discharge and death communications. *British Journal of Hospital Medicine*, **42** (1), 59–61

Fanshel, S. (1972). Meaningful measure of health for epidemiology. *International Journal of Epidemiology*, **1**, 319–37

Farrelly C., Evans K. T., Rhodes J., Source of referral and its effect on gastric ulcer management. *British Journal of Clinical Practice*, **40** (10), 411–12

Farrow, S. C., Charny, M. C. and Lewis, P. A. (1988). A survey of the appropriateness of the public's response to hypothetical medical problems. *Journal of the Royal College of General Practitioners*, **38** (314), 402–6

Feder, J., Hadley, J. and Mullner, R. (1984). Falling through the cracks: poverty, insurance coverage and hospital care for the poor, 1980 and 1982. *Milbank Memorial Fund Quarterly*, **62** (4), 544–66

Fitzpatrick, G., Neutra, R. and Gilbert, J. P. (1977). Cost-effectiveness of cholecystectomy for silent gallstones In Bunker, J. P., Barnes, B. A. and Mosteller, F. (Eds.), *Costs, Risks and Benfits of Surgery.* Oxford University Press, New York

Fordyce, A. J. W. and Phillips, R. (1970). Waiting list management by computer. *Hospital*, **66** (9), 303–5

Forsyth, G. and Logan, R. F. L. (1968). *Gateway or Dividing Line? A Study of Hospital Out-patients in the 1960s.* Oxford University Press, London

Fowkes, F. G. R., Page, S. M. and Phillips-Miles, D. (1983). Surgical manpower, beds and output in the NHS: 1967–1977. *British Journal of Surgery*, **70**, 114–16

Frankel, S. J. (1986). *The Huli Response to Illness.* Cambridge University Press

Frankel, S. J. (1989). The natural history of waiting lists: some wider explanations for an unnecessary problem. *Health Trends*, **21** (2), 56–8

Frankel, S. J. and Lewis, G. A. (Eds.) (1989). *A Continuing Trial of Treatment.* Kluwer Academic Publishers, Dortrecht

Frankel, S. J., Farrow, A. and West R. R. (1989). Non-attendance or non-invitation? A case control study of failed outpatient appointments. *British Medical Journal*, **298**, 1343–5.

Frankel S. J., Williams, M., Nanchahal, K., Coast, J. (1990). *Epidemiologically based assessments of need: total hip and knee joint replacement.* Bristol: Health Care Evaluation Unit

Frankel, S. J., Coast, J., Baker, A., Collins, C., (1991). Booked admission as a replacement for waiting lists in the new NHS. *British Medical Journal*, **303**, 1257–8

Frankel, S. J. (1991a). The Epidemiology of Indications. *Journal of Epidemiology & Community Medicine*, Editorial: 257–9

Frankel, S. J. (1991b). Health needs, health care requirements, and the myth of infinite demand. *The Lancet*, **337**, 1588–9

Frankenberg, R. (1988). 'Your time or mine?' An anthropological view of the tragic temporal contradictions of biomedical practice. In Young, M. and Schuller, T. (Eds.), *The Rhythms of Society*. Routledge, London

Fraser, R. C., Patterson, H. R. and Peacock, E. (1974). Referrals to hospitals in an East Midlands city – a medical audit. *Journal of the Royal College of General Practitioners*, **24**, 304–19

Freddi, G. (1989). Problems of organisational rationality in health systems: political controls and policy options. In Freddi, G. and Bjorkman, J. W. (Eds.), *Controlling Medical Professionals*. Sage, London

Frost, C. E. B. and Francis, B. J. (1979). Clinical decision-making: a study of general surgery within Trent RHA. *Social Science and Medicine*, **13A**, 193–8

Frost, C. E. B. (1980). How permanent are NHS waiting lists? *Social Science and Medicine*, **14C**, 1–11

Fry J. (1972). Twenty one years of general practice – changing patterns. *Journal of the Royal College of General Practitioners*, **22**, 521–8

Fry J. (1978). General practice now. 9: The GP-hospital interface. *Update*, **17** (9), 1119–20

Garrod, J. and Bennett, A. E. (1971). Validated interview schedule for use in population surveys of chronic disease and disability. *British Journal of Preventive and Social Medicine*, **25**, 97–104

Gazet, J. C., Rainsbury, R. M., Ford, H. T., Powles, T. J. and Coombes, R. C. (1985). Survey of treatment of primary breast cancer in Great Britain. *British Medical Journal*, **290**, 1793–5

Gillam, D· M. (1985). Referral to consultants – the National Health Service versus private practice. *Journal of the Royal College of General Practitioners*, **35**, 15–18

Gilson, B. S., Gilson, J. S., Bergner, M., Bobbit, R. A., Kressel, S., Pollard, W. E. and Vesselago. (1975). The Sickness Impact Profile. *American Journal of Public Health*, **65**, 1304–10

Glover, J. A. (1948). The paediatric approach to tonsillectomy. *Archives of Disease in Childhood*, **23**, 1–6

Goldacre, M. J., Lee, A. and Don, B. (1987). Waiting list statistics. 1: relation between admissions from waiting list and length of waiting list. *British Medical Journal*, **295**, 1105–8

Goran, M. (1979). The evolution of the PSRO hospital review system. *Medical Care*, **17** (suppl 5), 1–47

Government Statistical Service (1990). *Ordinary admissions, day care admissions, and regular day and night admissions. England 1989/90*. London: Department of Health

Government Statistical Service (1991a). *Outpatient and ward attenders, England, financial year 1989/90*. London: Department of Health

Government Statistical Service (1991b). Statistics of elective admissions and patients waiting: England, six months ending 31 March 1991. *Bulletin* **2** (7), Department of Health

Grace, J. F. and Armstrong, D. (1986). Reasons for referral to hospital: extent of agreement between the perceptions of patients, general practitioners and consultants. *Family Practice*, **3** (3), 143–7

Grace, J. F. and Armstrong, D. (1987). Referral to hospital: perceptions of patients, general practitioners and consultants about necessity and suitability of referral. *Family Practice*, **4** (3), 170–5

Green, D. G. (1986). *Challenge to the NHS*. IEA, London

Griffiths, M., Waters, W. E. and Acheson E. D. (1979). Variation in hospital stay after inguinal herniorrhaphy. *British Medical Journal*, **279**, 787–9

Griffiths, R. [Chairman]. *National Health Service Management Inquiry*. (1983). Department of Health and Social Security, London

Grogono, A. W. and Woodgate, D. J. (1971). Index for measuring health. *Lancet*, **ii**, 1024–6

Grol, R., Mokkink, H., Smits, A., Van Eijk, J., Beek, M., Mesker, P. and Mesker-Niesten, J. (1985). Work satisfaction of general practitioners and the quality of patient care. *Family Practice*, **2**, 128–35

Grol, R., Whitfield, M., De Maeseneer, J. and Mokkink, H. (1990). Attitudes to risk taking in medical decisions among British, Dutch and Belgian general practitioners. *British Journal of General Practice*, **40**, 134–6

Grossman, M. (1972). *The Demand for Health: a Theoretical and Empirical Investigation*. National Bureau of Economic Research Occasional Paper No. 119. Columbia University Press, New York and London

Grundy, F., Hitchens, R. A. N. and Lewis-Faning, E. (1956). *A Study of Hospital Waiting Lists in Cardiff (1953–1954)*. A report prepared for the Board of Governors of the United Cardiff Hospitals, Cardiff

Hall R., Roberts C. J., Coles G. A., Fisher D. J., Fowkes F. G. R., Jones J. H., Kilpatrick G. S., Lazarus J. H., Scanlon M. F., Picton Thomas J., The impact of guidelines in clinical outpatient practice. *Journal of the Royal College of Physicians of London*, **22** (4), 244–7

Hallam L. (1991). Organisation of telephone services and patients' access to doctors by telephone. *British Medical Journal*, **302**, 629–32

Hannay D. (1980). The iceberg of illness and 'trivial' consultations. *Journal of the Royal College of General Practitioners*, **30**, 51–4

Hansard [House of Lords]. (1889). Medical Institutions. 3rd Series, **338**, col. 1553–5. Hansard, London

Harley, M. (1988). Waiting times in trauma and orthopaedic surgery. *Community Medicine*, **10**, 57–65

Harris, J. (1988). More and better justice. In Bell, J. M. and Mendus, S. (Eds.), *Philosophy and Medical Welfare*. Cambridge University Press

Harris, W. M. (1969). Traumatic arthritis for hip after dislocation and acetabular fracture. *Journal of Joint and Bone Surgery*, **51**, 737–55

Hart, A. J., Edmond, P. and Varman, D. J. (1979). Postcards or outpatients: an alternative method of follow-up. *British Medical Journal*, **1**, 1321–1322

Health Services Board. (1977). *Common Waiting Lists for NHS and Private Patients in NHS Hospitals: Report by Health Services Board made under Section 6 of the Health Services Act 1976*. Cmnd 6828. Her Majesty's Stationery Office, London

Heasman, M. A. (1968). Scottish Hospital Inpatient Statistics. *Health Bulletin*, **26**, 10–18

Henderson, J., Goldacre, M. J., Griffith, M. and Simmonds, H. M. (1989). Day case surgery: geographical trends and readmission rates. *Journal of Epidemiology and Community Health*, **43** (3), 301–5

Heppenstall, I. (1985). Entering the twilight zone. *Health and Social Service Journal*, **94**, 982

Heyink, J. (1990). Adding years to your life or adding life to your years. QALY (Quality Adjusted Life Year): theoretical and practical issues. *International Journal of Health Sciences*, **1** (1), 45–9

Hicks, N. R. and Baker, I. A. (1991). General practitioners' opinions of health services available to their patients. *British Medical Journal*, **302**, 991–3

Higgins, J. (1988). *The Business of Medicine*. Macmillan Education, Basingstoke

Hildrew, P. (1987). Penalties sought for NHS delays. *The Guardian*, 17 September 1987

Hill M. N, Levine D. M, Whelton P. K. (1988) Awareness, use, and impact of the 1984 Joint National Committee Consensus Report on High Blood Pressure. *American Journal of Public Health*. **78**, 1190–4

Hill, J. D, Hampton, J. R. and Mitchell, J. R. A. (1978). A randomised trial of home versus hospital management for patients with suspected acute myocardial infarction. *Lancet*, **i**, 837–41

HMG (1946). *The National Health Service Act*. London: HMSO

Holland, W. W., Ipsen J. and Kostrzewski, J. (Eds.) (1979). *Measurement of Levels of Health*. World Health Organisation Regional Office for Europe, Copenhagen

Hollis, M. (1970). Reason and ritual. In Wilson, B. R. (Ed.), *Rationality*. Basil Blackwell, Oxford

Hopkins, A. (1976). Consultants' work load. *Lancet*, **i**, 956–8

Houghton, P. W. and Brodribb, A. J. (1989). Failure to attend for operation: a comparison between booked admissions and the waiting list system. *British Medical Journal*, **299**, 1139–40

House of Commons Health Committee (1991). *Public Expenditure on Health Services: Waiting Lists*. London: HMSO

Howie, J. G. R. (1977) Drug monitoring and adverse reactions. *British Medical Journal*. 1467

Hunt, S. M., McEwan, J. and McKenna, S. P. (1986). *Measuring Health Status*. Croom Helm, London

Inter-Authority Comparisons and Consultancy (1990). *Examining Some of England's Longest Waiting Lists*. Birmingham: Health Services Management Centre

Jacobs, L. G. H. and Pringle, M. A. (1990). Referral letters and replies from orthopaedic departments: opportunities missed. *British Medical Journal*,

301, 470–3

Jaffe, N. S. (1978). Cataract surgery – a modern attitude towards a technologic explosion. *New England Journal of Medicine*, **299**, 235–7

Janis, I. L. and Mason, L. (1977). *Decision-making. A Psychological Analysis of Conflict, Choice and Commitment.* The Free Press, New York

Jeffers, J. R., Bognanno, M. F. and Barlett, J. C. (1974). On the demand versus need for medical services and the concept of a 'shortage'. *American Journal of Public Health*, **61** (1), 46–63

Jennett, B. (1987). Waiting lists: a surgeon's response. *Lancet*, **i**, 796–7

Joensuu, H., Alanen, K. A. and Klemi, P. J. (1989). Doubts on 'curative' resection of pancreatic cancer. *Lancet*, **i**, 953–4

Jolly U., Think of the client. *Health Service Journal*, 23 November 1989, 1434–5

Jones, F. A. and McCarthy, M. (1978). Understanding waiting lists. *Lancet*, **ii**, 34–6

Jones, R. (1989). Variation in referral rates. *British Medical Journal*, **298**, 1099

Kahn, K. L., Kosecoff, J., Chassin, M. R., Flynn, M. F., Fink, A., Pattaphongse, N., Soloman, D. H. and Brook, R. H. (1988). Measuring the clinical appropriateness of the use of a procedure. Can we do it? *Medical Care*, **26** (4), 415–22

Kaplan, R., Bush, J. and Berry, C. (1976). Health status. *Health Services Research*, **11**, 478

Kiff, R. S. and Sykes, P. A. (1988). Who undertakes the consultations in the outpatient department? *British Medical Journal*, **296**, 1511–12

Kirk, R. M. (1976). Reducing outpatient attendances. *British Medical Journal*, **1**, 1521–2

Lakhani, S., Leach, R. D. and Jarrett, P. E. M. (1987). Effect of a surgical day unit on waiting lists. *Journal of the Royal Society of Medicine*, **80**, 628–9

Lancet Sanitary Commission. (1866). *Report of the* Lancet *Sanitary Commission for Investigating the State of the Infirmaries of Workhouses*. London

Larson, C. B. (1963). Rating scales for hip disabilities. *Clinical Orthopaedics*, **31**, 85–93

Laslett, P. (1977). *Family Life and Illicit Love in Earlier Generations*. Cambridge University Press

Last, J. M. (1963). The iceberg: completing the clinical picture in general practice. *Lancet*, **ii**, 28–31

Laurance, J. (1988). Hospital waiting lists rise again. *The Sunday Times*, 13 November 1988, 1

Lee, A. (1966). *Applied Queuing Theory*. Macmillan, Toronto

Lee, A., Don, B. and Goldacre, M. (1987). Waiting list statistics. II: an estimate of inflation of waiting list length. *British Medical Journal*, **295**, 1197–8

Leech, and Luckman J. (1970). *Patients, Hospitals and Operations Research*. Tavistock Publications, London

Lees, D. S. (1976). Economics and non-economics of health services. *Three Banks Review*, **110**, 3–20

Leeuwenhorst Working Party. (1974). *The general practitioner in Europe. A statement by the working party appointed by the Second European Conference on the Teaching of General Practice*. Leeuwenhorst, Netherlands

Lester, J. P. (1980). Why not reclaim our patients from hospital outpatient clinics? *Journal of the Royal College of General Practitioners*, **30** (213), 230

Lewin, K. (1958). Group decision and social change. In Maccoby, E. E. *et al*. (Eds.), *Readings in Social Psychology*, 3rd edition. Holt, Rinehart and Winston, New York

Lewis, C. E. (1969). Variations in the incidence of surgery. *New England Journal of Medicine*, **281**, 880–4

Lewis, E. B. (1981). Private practice. *British Medical Journal*, **282**, 841–842

Light D. (1990) Medical house arrest. *The Health Service Journal*, **100**, 1 November, 1648–9

Lindsay, C. M. and Feigenbaum, B. (1984). Rationing by waiting lists. *American Economic Review*, **74** (3), 405–17

Lomas J., Anderson G. M., Domnick-Pierre K., Vayda E., Enkin M. W., Hannah W. J. (1989) Do practice guidelines guide practice? *New England Journal of Medicine*, **321**, 1306–11

Loudon, I. S. (1976). A question of numbers. *Lancet*, **i**, 736–7

Lourie, J. A (1978). Notes on an orthopaedic waiting list. *British Journal of Clinical Practice*, **32**, 224–5

Luckman, J., McKenzie, M. and Stringer, J. C. (1969). *Management Policies for Large Ward Units*. Health Report No. 1. Institute of Operational Research, London

Lydeard, S. and Jones, R. (1989). Factors affecting the decision to consult with dyspepsia: comparison of consulters with non-consulters. *Journal of the Royal College of General Practitioners*, **39**, 495–8

Marinker, M., Wilkin, D. and Metcalfe, D. H. (1988). Referral to hospital: can we do better? *British Medical Journal*, **297**, 461–4

Marsh, G. N. and McNay, R. A. (1974). Factors affecting workload in general practice – II. *British Medical Journal*, **1**, 319–21

Marsh G. N., Are follow-up consultations at medical outpatient departments futile? *British Medical Journal*, **284**, 17 April 1982: 1176–7

Mason, A. (1976). An epidemiological approach to the monitoring of hospital waiting list statistics. *Proceedings of the Royal Society of Medicine*, **69**, 939–42

Mather, H. G., Pearson, N. G., Read, K. L. Q. *et al*. (1971). Acute myocardial infarction: Home and hospital treatment. *British Medical Journal*, **3**, 334–8

McCormack T. T., Collier J. A., Abel P. D., Collins C. D., Ritchie W. N. (1984). Attitudes to follow-up after uncomplicated surgery – hospital out-patients or general practitioner? *Health Trends*, **16**,46–7

McDowell, I. and Newell, C. (1987). *Measuring Health: a Guide to Rating Scales and Questionnaires*. Oxford University Press

McGlade, K. J., Bradley, T., Murphy, G. J. and Lundy, G. P. (1988). Referrals to hospital by general practitioners: a study of compliance and communication. *British Medical Journal*, **297**, 1246–8

McMullan, J. J. and Barr, A. (1964). Outpatient letters. A study in communication. *Journal of the Royal College of General Practitioners*, **7**, 66–75

McPherson, K., Strong, P. M., Epstein, A. and Jones, L. (1981). Regional variations in the use of common surgical procedures within and between England and Wales, Canada and the United States of America. *Social Science and Medicine*, **15A**, 273–88

McPherson, K., Wennberg, J. E., Hovind, O. B. and Clifford, P. (1982). Small area variation in the use of common surgical procedures: an international comparison of New England, England and Norway. *New England Journal of Medicine*, **307**, 1310–14

McPherson, K., Coulter, A. and Stratton, I. (1985a). Increasing use of private practice by patients in Oxford requiring common elective surgical operations. *British Medical Journal*, **291**, 797–9

McPherson, K., Strong, P. M., Jones, J. and Britton, B. J. (1985b). Do cholecystectomy rates correlate with geographic variations in the prevalence of gallstones. *Journal of Epidemiology and Community Health*, **39**, 179–82

Mechanic, D. (1986). The concept of illness behaviour: culture, situation and personal predisposition. *Psychological Medicine*, **16**, 1–7

Metcalfe, D. H. H. (1990). *Essential institutional competences for population-based education.* Paper presented to Royal Society of Medicine Fondation / Macy Foundation Conference on Medical Education in Canada, the UK and USA. Turnberry Isle, Florida

Middleton, W. G. and McHardy, G. J. (1976). Follow-up needed? *Lancet*, **i**, 972

Ministry of Health. (1938). *Nineteenth Annual Report of the Ministry of Health, 1937–38.* His Majesty's Stationery Office, London

Ministry of Health. (1962). *Admissions to Hospitals and Hospital Waiting Lists, enclosing Memoranda on (1) Admission to Hospital and Domiciliary Care and (2) Hospital Waiting Lists.* HM (62) 45K. Ministry of Health, London

Ministry of Health. (1963). *Reduction of Waiting Lists, Surgical and General.* HM (63) 22. Ministry of Health, London

Mooney, G. and Olsen, J. A. (1991). QALYs: Where next? pp 120–40 in McGuire, A., Fenn, P. and Mayhew, K. (Eds). *Providing Health Care: The Economics of Alternative Systems of Finance and Delivery.* Oxford University Press, Oxford

Moore, A. T. and Roland, M. O. (1989). How much variation in referral rates among general practitioners is due to chance? *British Medical Journal*, **298**, 500–2

Mordue, A. and Kirkup, B. (1989). An appraisal of waiting list problems. *Health Trends*, **2**, 110–14

Morgan, M., Mays, N. and Holland, W. (1987a). Can hospital use be a measure of need for health care? *Journal of Epidemiology and Community Health*, **41**, 269–74

Morgan, M., Paul, E. and Devlin, H. B. (1987b). Length of stay for common surgical procedures: variation among districts. *British Journal of Surgery*, **74**, 884–9

Morgan, M. (1988). Variations in length of stay at district level. In Ham, C. (Ed.), *Health Care Variations: Assessing the Evidence.* King's Fund, London

Morgan, M. and Beech, R. (1990). Variations in lengths of stay and rates of day case surgery: implications for the efficiency of surgical management. *Journal of Epidemiology and Community Health, 1990*, **44** (2), 90–105

Morrell, D. C., Gage, H. G. and Robinson, N. A. (1971). Referral to hospital by general practitioners. *Journal of the Royal College of General Practitioners*, **21**, 77–85

Morris, D. (1984). Surgical waiting lists. *British Medical Journal*, **289**, 271–2

Morris, D., Ward, A. W. M. and Handyside, A. J. (1968). Early discharge after hernia repair. *Lancet*, **i**, 681–5

Morris, G. E. and Jarrett, P. E. M. (1987). Recurrence rates following local anaesthetic day case inguinal hernia repair by junior surgeons in a district general hospital. *Annals of the Royal College of Surgeons of England,* **69**, 97–9

Mozes, B., Halkin, H., Katz, A., Schiff, E. and Modan, B. (1987). Reduction of redundant hospital stay through controlled intervention. *Lancet,* **i**, 968–9

National Audit Office. (1987). *Use of Operating Theatres in the National Health Service.* Her Majesty's Stationery Office, London

National Health Service Act. (1946). His Majesty's Stationery Office, London

National Health Service and Community Care Act (1990). Her Majesty's Stationery Office, London

Neuhauser, D. (1977). Elective inguinal herniorrhaphy versus truss in the elderly. In Bunker, J. P., Barnes, B. A. and Mosteller, F. (Eds.), *Costs, Risks and Benefits of Surgery.* Oxford University Press, New York

Newman, C. (1957). *The Evolution of Medical Education in the Nineteenth Century.* Oxford

Noone, A., Goldacre, M., Coulter, A. and Seagroatt, V. (1989). Do referral rates vary widely between practices and does supply of services affect demand? A study in Milton Keynes and the Oxford region. *Journal of the Royal College of General Practitioners,* **39**, 404–7

Ogg, T. W. and Obey, P. A. (1987). The workload of a purpose built day surgical unit. *Annals of the Royal College of Surgeons of England,* **69**, 110–12

Olsen N. D. L., (1976). A question of numbers. *Lancet,* **i**, 853–4 [Correspondence]

Oregon Health Services Commission. (1991). *Prioritization of Health Services: A Report to the Governor and Legislature.* Oregon Health Services Commission, Salem

Pauly, M. V. (1979). What is unnecessary surgery? *Milbank Memorial Fund Quarterly,* **57**, 95–117

Payer, L. (1988). *Medicine and Culture. Varieties of Treatment in the United States, England, West Germany and France.* Henry Holt and Company, New York

Payne, S., Ramaiah, R. S. and Jones, D. T. (1987). Open access to orthopaedic appliances for general practitioners. *British Medical Journal,* **294**, 485–6

Pearson, G. (1983). *Hooligan: A History of Respectable Fears.* Macmillan Press, London

Pearson, R. J. C., Smedby, B., Berfenstam, R., Logan, R. F. L., Burgess, A. M. and Peterson, O. L. (1968). Hospital caseloads in Liverpool, New England, and Uppsala. *Lancet,* **ii**, 559–66

Phoenix, C. J. (1971). Waiting list management and admission scheduling. In Abrams, M. (Ed.), *Spectrum 1971* Conference on Medical Computing. Butterworths, London

Pineault, R., Contandriopoulos, A. P., Valois, M., Bastian, M. L. and Lance, J. M. (1985). Randomized clinical trial of one-day surgery: patient satisfaction, clinical outcomes and costs. Medical Care, **23** (2), 171–82

Pinker, R. (1966). *English Hospital Statistics 1861–1938.* Heinemann, London

Porter, K. M. (1985). Orthopaedic audit – review of inpatient waiting lists. *British Medical Journal,* **291**, 1216–17

Powell, J. E. (1966). *A New Look at Medicine and Politics*. Pitman Medical Publishing, London

Preston-Whyte, M. E., Fraser, R. C. and Beckett, J. L. (1983). Effect of a principal's gender on consultation patterns. *Journal of the Royal College of General Practitioners*, **33**, 654–8

Priest W. M., Lond M. D., A thousand outpatients. *Lancet*, **ii**, 1043–7

Private Patients' Plan. (1984). *Private Hospital Plan*. Private Patients' Plan Ltd., London

Roland, M. O, Middleton, J., Goss, B. and Moore, A. T. (1989). Should performance indicators in general practice relate to whole practices or to individual doctors? *Journal of the Royal College of General Practitioners*, **39**, 461–2

Roos, N. P., Roos, L. L. and Henteleff, P. D. (1977). Elective surgical rates – do high rates mean lower standards? *New England Journal of Medicine*, **297**, 360–5

Roos, N. P. and Roos, L. L. (1982). Surgical rate variations: do they reflect the health or socioeconomic characteristics of the population. *Medical Care*, **20**, 945–58

Roos, N. P. (1984). Hysterectomy: variations in rates across small areas and across physicians' practices. *American Journal of Public Health*, **74**, 327–35

Roos, N. P., Wennberg, J. E., Malenka, D. J., Fisher, E. S., McPherson, K., Anderson, T. F., Cohen, M. M. and Ramsey, E. (1989). Mortality and reoperation after open and transurethral resection of the prostate for benign prostatic hyperplasia. *New England Journal of Medicine*, **320** (17), 1120–4

Ross H., Castledine D., Herbert J. A farewell to queues. *Health Service Journal*, 13 July 1989, 851–2

Rosser, R. and Watts, V. C. (1972). Measurement of hospital output. *International Journal of Epidemiology*, **1**, 361–8

Rothert, M. L., Rovner, D. R., Elstein, A. S., Holzman, G. B., Holmes, M. M. and Ravitch, M. M. (1984). Differences in medical referral decisions for obesity among family practitioners, general internists and gynaecologists. *Medical Care*, **22**, 42–53

Royal College of General Practitioners, Office of Population Censuses and Surveys. (1979). *Morbidity Statistics from General Practice, 1971–2. Second National Survey. Studies on medical and population subjects No 36.* Her Majesty's Stationery Office, London

Royal College of Surgeons of England. (1985). *Commission on the Provision of Surgical Services: Guidelines for Day Case Surgery*. Royal College of Surgeons, London

Royal Commission on Poor Laws. (1905–9). *Report*. (Majority)

Russell, I. T., Brendan Devlin, H., Fell, M. *et al.* Day Case Surgery for Hernias and Haemorrhoids, *The Lancet*, **i**, 16 April

Sanderson, H. F. (1982). What's in a waiting list? *British Medical Journal*, **285**, 1368–9

Sandler, D. A., Mitchell, J. R., Fellows, A. and Garner, S. T. (1989). Is an information booklet for patients leaving hospital helpful and useful? *British Medical Journal*, **298**, 870–4

Scambler, A., Scambler, G. and Craig, D. (1981). Kinship and friendship networks and women's demand for primary care. *Journal of the Royal College of General Practitioners*, **31** (233), 746–50

Schneeweiss, R., Ellsbury, K., Hart, L. G. and Geyman, J. P. (1989). The economic impact and multiplier effect of a family practice clinic on an academic medical center. *Journal of the American Medical Association*, **262**, 370–5

Schroeder, S. A. (1984). Western European responses to physician oversupply. *Journal of the American Medical Association*, **252**, 373–84

Scott, R. and Gilmore, M. (1966). The Edinburgh hospitals. In McLachlan, G. (Ed.), *Problems and Progress in Medical Care*. Oxford University Press, London

Secretary of State for Health. (1989). *Working For Patients*. Her Majesty's Stationery Office, London

Shaw C. D., (1981) The problems of out-patient visits. *Health Trends*, **13**: 107–8

Shortell, S. M. and McNerney, W. J. (1990). Criteria and guidelines for reforming the United States health care system. *New England Journal of Medicine*, **322** (7), 463–7

Shryock, R. H. (1979). *The Development of Modern Medicine: an Interpretation of the Social and Scientific Facts Involved*. The University of Wisconsin Press, Madison

Silverman D. (1987) *Communications and Medical Practice: Social Relations in the Clinic*. London: Sage

Sjønell, G. (1986). Effect of establishing a primary health care centre on the utilization of primary health care and other outpatient care in a Swedish Urban Area. *Family Practice*, **3**, 148–54

Sjønell, G. (1990). *Access in primary health care*. Paper presented to the first WONCA European Regional Conference, Barcelona

Sloan, F. A. and Valvona, J. (1986). Why has hospital length of stay declined? An evaluation of alternative theories. *Social Science and Medicine*, **22**, 63–73

Smith, C. H. and Armstrong, D. (1989). Comparison of criteria derived by government and patients for evaluating general practitioner services. *British Medical Journal*, **299**, 494–6

Smith, G. T. (Ed.) (1988). *Measuring Health: a Practical Approach*. Wiley, Chichester

Sorensen, H. T. and Christensen, B. (1986). Referrals from general practice to specialists in Denmark. *Journal of the Royal College of General Practitioners*, **36**, 290–1

Southam, J. A. and Talbot, R. W. (1980). Planned surgical admissions in a district hospital. *British Medical Journal*, **280**, 808–9

Sparks D., A firm decision to save time. *Health Services Journal*, **98**, 3 March 1988, 278

Spicer, M. W. (1982). The economics of bureaucracy and the British National Health Service. *Milbank Memorial Fund Quarterly*, **6**, 657–72

Starey, C. J. H. (1961). A hospital outpatient referral study. *Journal of the Royal College of General Practitioners*, **4**, 214–22

Steering Group on Health Services Information. (1982). *A Report on the Collection and Use of Information about Hospital Clinical Activity in the National Health Service*. Her Majesty's Stationery office, London

Stevens D. L., Outpatient waiting lists. *British Journal of Hospital Medicine*, **40**, October 1985, 197 [Editorial]

Stoll, B. A. (1988). Balancing costs and benefits in treatment of late cancer. *Lancet*, **i**, 579–80

Strang J. R., Cone-Smith J. R., Outpatient follow-up: why bother? *Hospital Update*, May 1989, 321–2

Suchman, E. A. (1967). Health attitudes and behaviour. A model for research on community health campaigns. *Journal of Health and Social Behaviour*, **8**, 197–209

Sykes, P. A. (1986). DHSS waiting list statistics – a major deception? *British Medical Journal*, **293**, 1038–9

Torrance, G. W. (1976). Health status index model: a unified mathematical view. Management Science, **22**, 990

Townsend, P. and Davidson, N. (1982). *Inequalities in Health. The Black Report*. Penguin Books, Harmondsworth

Vayda, E . (1973). A comparison of surgical rates in Canada and in England and Wales. *New England Journal of Medicine*, **289**, 1224–9

Wadsworth, M., Butterfield, W. and Blaney, R. (1971). *Health and Sickness: the Choice of Treatment*. Tavistock, London

Weaver, P. G. (1981). Waiting list: the neglected statistic. *Dimensions in Health Service*, **58** (5), 34–7

Wennberg, J. and Gittelsohn, A. (1982). Variations in medical care among small areas. Scientific American, **246**, 100–12

Wennberg, J. E. (1985). On patient need, equity, supplier-induced demand, and the need to assess the outcome of common medical practices. *Medical Care*, **23**, 512–20

Wennberg, J. E., Freeman, J. L. and Culp, W. J. (1987a). Are hospital services rationed in New Haven or over-utilised in Boston? *Lancet*, **i**, 1185–9

Wennberg, J. E. (1987b). Population illness rates do not explain population hospitalisation rates. *Medical Care*, **25**, 354–9

Wennberg, J. E. (1988). Practice variations and the need for outcomes research. In Ham, C. (Ed.), *Health Care Variations: Assessing the Evidence*. King's Fund Institute, London

Wennberg, J. E., Bunker, J. P. and Barnes, B. (1980). The need for assessing the outcome of common surgical practices. *Annual Review of Public Health*, **1**, 277–95

West, R. R. (1970). *Outpatient Waiting List Survey*. Welsh Hospital Board, Cardiff

West. R. R. (1987). Interpreting government statistics on acute hospital care (editorial). *British Medical Journal*, **295**, 509–10.

West, R. R., Farrow, S. C. and Adams Jones, D. (1988). Input-output relationships in the NHS: inter district variations in ENT surgery within Wales. *Community Medicine*, **10**, 319–27

West, R. R., Frankel, S. J. and Roberts, R. E. (1991). Waiting for general surgery; a question of priorities. *Journal of Management in Medicine*, **5**, 79–86.

West, R. R. and Jenkins, R. M. (1984). Problems of patients waiting for orthopaedic out-patient appointments. *Hospital and Health Services Review*, **80**, 126–30

West, R. R. and McKibbin, B. (1982). Shortening waiting lists in orthopaedic surgery outpatient clinics. *British Medical Journal*, **284**, 728–30

White, A. (1980). Waiting lists: a step towards representation, clarification, and solving of information problems. *Hospital and Health Services Review*, **76**, 270–74

WHO. (1978). *Definition of Health*. WHO, Geneva

Wijkel, D. (1986). Lower referral rates for integrated health centres in The Netherlands. *Health Policy*, **6**, 185–98

Wilcock, G. K. (1979). Economic aspects of the demand for total hip replacement in the elderly. *Age Ageing*, 8 (1), 32–5.

Wilkin, D. and Smith, A. (1987a). Explaining variation in general practitioner referrals to hospital. *Family Practice*, **4**, 160–9

Wilkin, D. and Smith, A. (1987b). Variation in general practitioners' referral rates to consultants. *Journal of the Royal College of General Practitioners*, **37**, 350–3

Williams, A. (1974). Measuring effectiveness of health care systems. *British Journal of Preventive and Social Medicine*, **28**, 196–202

Williams, A. and Anderson, R. (1975). *Efficiency in the Social Services*. Basil Blackwell, Oxford

Williams, D. R. R., West, R. J. and Hagard, S. (1983). Waiting list monitoring using information from hospital activity analysis and SBH 203 returns. *Community Medicine*, **5**, 311–16

Williams, A. (1985). Economics of coronary artery bypass grafting. *British Medical Journal*, **291**, 326–9

Williams, A. (1988). Applications in management. In Teeling Smith, G. F. (Ed.), *Measuring Health: A Practical Approach*. Wiley, London.

Williams, A. Escape the Trap. *The Health Service Journal*, 15 February 1990, 242–3

Williams, W. O. (1970). *A Study of General Practitioners' Workload in South Wales, 1965–66. Report from General Practice No. 12*. Royal College of General Practitioners, London

Winston, W. L. (1987). *Operations Research: Applications and Algorithms*. Duxbury Press, Boston

Working Group on Inequalities in Health. (1980). [Chairman: Sir Douglas Black.] *Report*. Department of Health and Social Security, London

Wortman R., Vinokur A., Sechrest L. (1988) Do consensus conferences work? A process evaluation of the NIH consensus development program. *Journal Health Politics Policy & Law*, **13**, 469–98.

Wright, H. J. (1968). *General Practice in South West England. Report from General Practice No. 7*. Royal College of General Practitioners, London

Yates, J. (1987). *Why Are We Waiting?*. Oxford University Press

Zadik F. R. A question of numbers. *Lancet*, **i**, 853 [Correspondence]

Zola, I. K. (1973). Pathways to the doctor: from person to patient. *Social Science and Medicine*, **7**, 677–89

Index